THE NEW GOLDEN BOOK OF
ASTRONOMY

An Introduction to the Wonders of Space

by ROSE WYLER *and* GERALD AMES

Edited and with a Foreword by Donald H. Menzel, Director of Harvard College Observatory

Illustrated by John Polgreen
Additional illustrations for this edition by George Solonevich

GOLDEN PRESS · NEW YORK

PICTURE CREDITS

Yerkes Observatory: 13 bottom left, 83 right.
Lowell Observatory: 65 top right (both).
Mt. Wilson and Palomar Observatories: 80 bottom (both), 86 top (all).
© The California Institute of Technology: 81 top and bottom right.
Lick Observatory: 84 bottom left, 85 top right.
National Aeronautics and Space Administration: 103 bottom.

Ring around the Moon, made by moonlight shining through a thin cloud

Opposite page: *On the Moon, a 150-pound man will weigh only 25 pounds*

Library of Congress Catalog Card Number: 65-12334

1969 Edition

Third printing, 1969

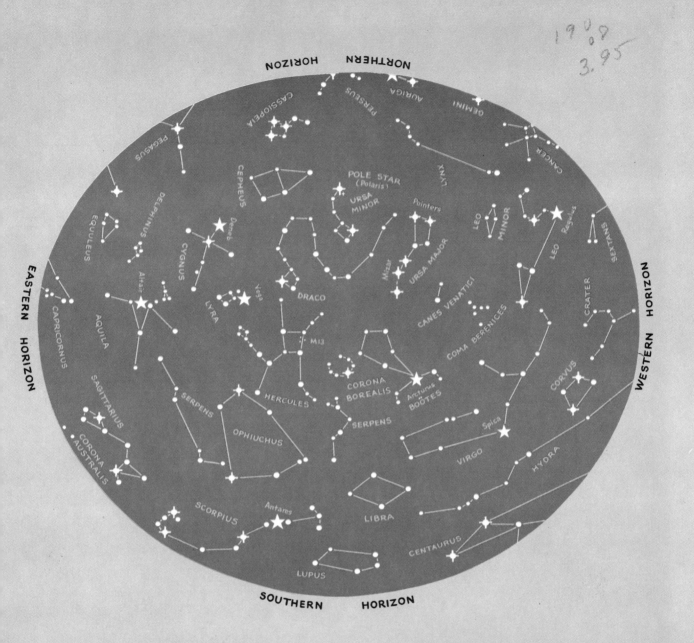

CONSTELLATIONS OF SUMMER

ABOUT 9 P.M. IN JULY IN MOST OF THE NORTHERN HEMISPHERE

Hold chart overhead with the words NORTHERN HORIZON *toward north.*

STARS

1st magnitude	★
2nd magnitude	✦
3rd magnitude	●
Fainter	·
Star clusters and nebulae	∴

OTHER INTERESTING OBJECTS

Globular star cluster M13 in HERCULES

COMA BERENICES star cluster

Star clouds and coal sacks
between CYGNUS and SAGITTARIUS

Mizar with faint companion

CONTENTS

Eratosthenes measured the Earth with a shadow

Copernicus found that the Earth circles the Sun

FOREWORD
by
DONALD H. MENZEL

Director, Harvard College Observatory
Author of A Field Guide to the Stars and Planets,
published by Houghton Mifflin Company, Boston

How exciting it is to live in the age of space exploration! While telescopes probe the far reaches of the Universe, artificial satellites observe the Sun and nearby space. Orbiting instruments send back information about the planets. Others are sent to survey the Moon, in preparation for landings by man.

Because the lunar sky is always perfectly clear and black, even in daytime, the Moon will be a good place for an observatory. Astronomers aim to place telescopes there for studying the stars, especially our own star, the Sun.

The Sun continually shoots vast clouds of atoms into space. Sometimes these clouds collide with the Earth and become trapped in its magnetic field. Occasionally atoms spill into the Earth's atmosphere around the poles, setting the air aglow with the northern and southern lights. The speeding particles may be dangerous to astronauts. For this and other reasons, scientists are carefully investigating the Sun's activity.

Each of the planets circling the Sun has its own interesting features. Bright Venus changes shape like the Moon. Clouds always hide its solid surface, but radio waves from deep in Venus' atmosphere give some infor-

Galileo, first to use the telescope for astronomy

Newton discovered the law of gravitation

mation about the planet's surface. It is very hot, perhaps with a temperature of 800 degrees Fahrenheit.

At the other extreme are the cold giants, Jupiter and Saturn. Saturn is the planet with the beautiful rings. Jupiter has many moons, four of which are large and bright enough to be seen with a small telescope or binocular.

The planet Mars is a tempting world for future astronauts to visit. They will find the answers to many questions. Are those mysterious grey-green areas some form of plant life? Do any animals exist on Mars? Astronomers generally agree that Mars, of all the planets of the solar system, is the one most likely to sustain life.

At night we see thousands of stars in the sky. These stars are suns, some of them larger and brighter than our Sun. The stars seem small and faint only because they are so very far away.

In addition to the stars that we can see with the unaided eye, there are perhaps a hundred thousand million more. Through a telescope, the hazy glow of the Milky Way becomes a rich pattern of stars.

In these pages you will read of the many wonders of the heavens. You will learn how astronomers today are adding to the knowledge gained by sky watchers of the past.

Read the great story of astronomy, but also do more than read. Become a sky watcher yourself. When the night is dark and clear, go out of doors and become acquainted with the stars. Make the constellations your friends. I am sure you will find the study of astronomy a great and exciting adventure. As you explore the sky, you follow in the footsteps of the men and women who have observed its wonders in the past. You join the company of the astronomers who are probing its mysteries today.

Earth and Moon revolve around a star called the Sun

PART ONE

Our World in Space

WINDOW OF THE SKY

Would you like to explore space far above the Earth? You can do this without leaving the ground. No matter where you live, you can look through a window into space. You can look into the sky and make discoveries, if you know how to look and what to see.

In daytime, the Sun is in the sky, and sometimes you can see the Moon. No stars are visible, because the sky is too bright for them to be seen. But the stars are always there.

All day long the Sun moves across the sky. That is the way it seems, but of course the Sun does not really move. Suppose you are on a ship, waiting to sail. Suddenly the land begins to drift away from the ship. But you know this is impossible! The land is not moving. The ship has begun to move away from the land.

So it is with the Sun and the Earth. The Sun is still; the Earth is moving. It is rotating—spinning like a top. It spins around an imaginary line, the axis, which runs through the Earth from pole to pole. You do not notice the motion, since everything around you is moving the same way.

The Earth spins toward the east. Because of this, the Sun seems to move toward the west. At sunset, your part of the Earth is turning away from the Sun.

For a while the sky stays bright, and its brightness hides the fainter light of the stars. Then the Earth moves you around into its own shadow—the shadow called night.

The darkening sky becomes a window. You look through it into space, and see what was hidden before. A few bright stars appear; soon there are hundreds, and later a few thousand.

It is easy to picture the sky as a great dome with the stars fixed upon it. As you watch, the dome and all the stars seem to be turning. The motion is from east to west. New stars rise in the east while others set in the west. Of course, the stars only seem to move because the Earth is turning under them.

As the Earth spins, one side faces the Sun and has day; the other side is in the shadow of night

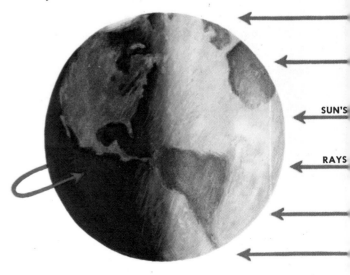

SUN'S

RAYS

11

The Earth's axis points toward the North Pole of the sky. The North Star is near the Pole

TURNING WHEEL OF STARS

The sky is all around our ball-shaped Earth, but only half of it can be seen from one place at one time. The other half is hidden by the Earth itself. If we happen to be right at the North Pole, we can see all the northern half of the sky but none of the southern half. If we live in the northern hemisphere between the Pole and the Equator, we see part of the northern half of the sky and part of the southern half.

As we watch the northern sky at night, it seems to be turning like a wheel. This motion can be photographed. A camera is aimed at the sky, and the film is exposed for an hour or more. When the picture is developed, it shows lines of light curving around a central point. These are star tracks, caused by the turning of the Earth and the camera.

Imagine the Earth's axis stretching out from the North Pole into the sky. It points right to the center of the wheel

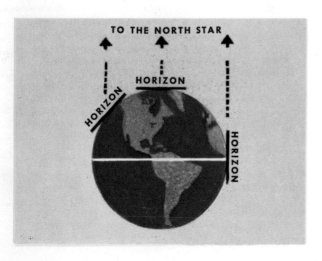

The farther north you are in the northern hemisphere, the higher the North Star above the horizon

12

of stars. That spot is the North Pole of the sky.

Very near the sky's North Pole is a famous and useful star. We call it the Pole Star or North Star. It shows us which direction is north. And it shows us how far north we are on the Earth. If the North Star is right overhead, we are at the North Pole. If it is on the horizon, we are at the Equator. If it is half way up in the sky, we are half way between the Pole and the Equator.

It is easy to locate the North Star. First we look for a well-known group of stars, the Big Dipper. It is made up of seven bright stars. Three form the handle and four the bowl. The two stars of the bowl farthest from the handle are called the Pointers, because they point to the North Star. Connect the Pointers with an imaginary line, and run it out from the top of the bowl as far as about five times the distance between the Pointers.

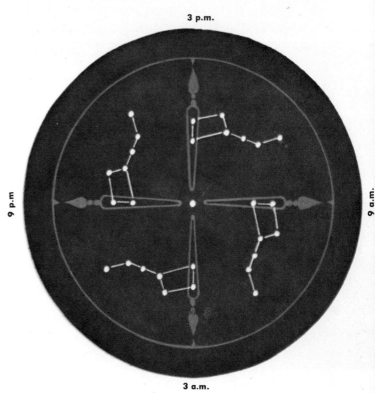

CLOCK IN THE SKY. *The Big Dipper circles the North Star every 24 hours. The diagram shows its positions at different hours on July 15*

There you come to a star somewhat fainter than the Pointers. This is the North Star.

From the northern part of the Earth the Dipper can be seen all night long. It never sets. During the night it seems to swing half way around the sky. If it were visible in daytime we could watch it complete a circle around the North Star.

The Dipper and the North Star make a clock in the sky. The North Star is at the center. The Pointers are on the hour hand. In six hours the hand goes a quarter of the way around the clock; in twelve hours, half way; in twenty-four hours, all the way around.

Above the southern half of the Earth, different stars shine. They seem to circle the South Pole of the sky, but that Pole is not marked by any star. It is just a point in the darkness of space.

A time exposure shows the apparent motion of stars around the sky's North Pole

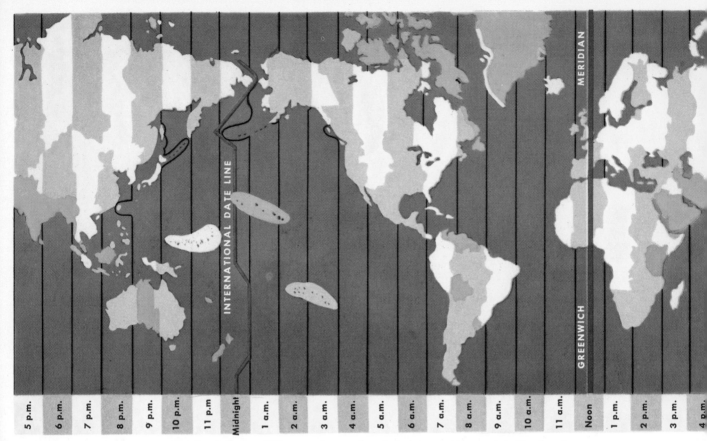

PLANETARY CLOCK

The best of all clocks is the Earth itself. Because its rotation causes the Sun to cross the sky, we can tell the time of day by noting the Sun's position. When it has reached its highest point, the time is noon. Twelve hours later it is midnight, when one day ends and another begins.

Long ago each town kept its own local time. It was noon there when the Sun was highest. At places to the east it was past noon; to the west it was before noon.

Local time keeping worked well enough before there were railroads and steamships. But later, when people began to travel fast and far, local time keeping caused confusion. How could a trip be planned when time changed from city to city and from country to country?

It became necessary to have one system of time keeping for the whole world. The problem was discussed among nations, and they agreed upon a system. It is called standard time. The world is divided into 24 zones by lines running north and south. For convenience, the lines in some places follow the borders of countries or states.

Time keeping starts at the line that runs through Greenwich, England. When the Sun is at its highest point there, it is 12 o'clock noon, Greenwich time. In the next zone to the west, it is

14

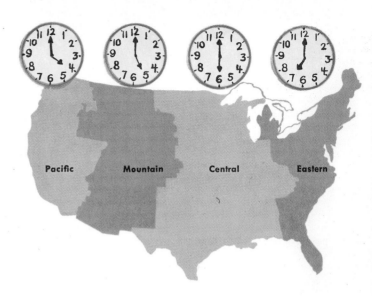

The United States from Maine to California has four time zones

Pacific   Mountain   Central   Eastern

11 A. M.; in the next zone, 10, and so on. In New York City it is 7 A. M., five hours earlier than at Greenwich, because New York lies in the fifth zone west of Greenwich.

In the zone on the opposite side of the world from Greenwich, it is midnight at Greenwich's noon. In the next zone to the west it is 11 P. M. of the day before.

By agreement, an International Date Line has been located in the zone opposite Greenwich. West of the line, the date is one day earlier than east of it. Each new day begins at the International Date Line. If you fly across that line, you must change your calendar date as well as your hour. If you cross it westward, you fly into yesterday; if you cross it eastward, you fly into tomorrow.

People set clocks, but the Earth keeps time. It is our great master clock, endlessly spinning and measuring our days.

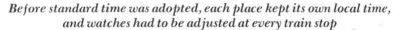

Before standard time was adopted, each place kept its own local time, and watches had to be adjusted at every train stop

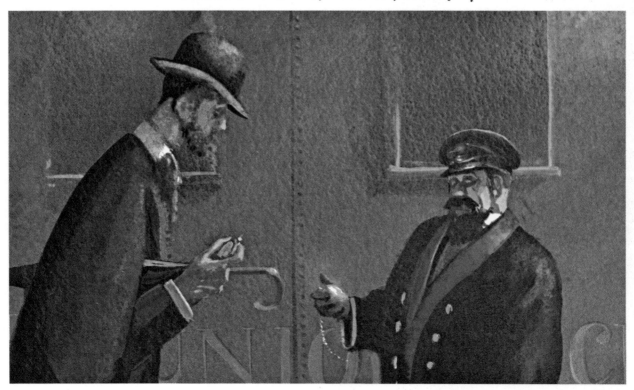

15

THE EARTH'S STRONG PULL

Several centuries ago, almost all people thought the Earth was as flat as it looks. They were afraid that if they traveled too far they might come to an edge and fall off. It was hard for them to imagine that they lived on a sphere—a ball in the sky. What would hold things on the "bottom" of such an Earth?

You know the answer. Things are held on the Earth by gravity. Gravity is a force pulling toward the Earth's center. That direction is *down,* everywhere on Earth. *Up* is away from the Earth's center.

Lift a stone and you feel the Earth's pull. You feel the weight of the stone, which is caused by gravity. If the stone weighs five pounds, that is because the Earth is pulling on it with five pounds of force. On the Moon the stone would weigh less because the force of gravity is less.

Drop a ball or other object and it falls faster and faster. This was proved over 300 years ago by the Italian scientist Galileo. But Galileo could not explain *why* the speed of a falling body increases. Later the British scientist Isaac Newton took up this question.

Newton discovered that a force of attraction—gravitation—is at work between any two bodies wherever they are. In the case of the falling ball, one body is the ball; the other is the Earth. Gravity pulls the ball toward the Earth. When it has fallen a foot, it is going at a certain speed. Meanwhile, gravity continues to pull, so the ball falls faster and faster.

Gravity and Orbits

Can you imagine throwing a ball around the Earth? This cannot happen on the Earth as it is, but it could happen if certain conditions were changed. You will have to imagine two very big changes. In the first place, the Earth would have to be without air. Otherwise the air would slow down your ball as it slows anything going through it. On an airless world your ball would not slow down. It would keep on going at the speed of your throw.

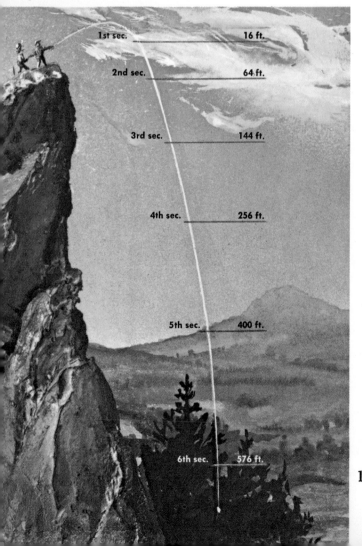

1st sec.   16 ft.
2nd sec.   64 ft.
3rd sec.   144 ft.
4th sec.   256 ft.
5th sec.   400 ft.
6th sec.   576 ft.

A falling object goes faster and faster

16

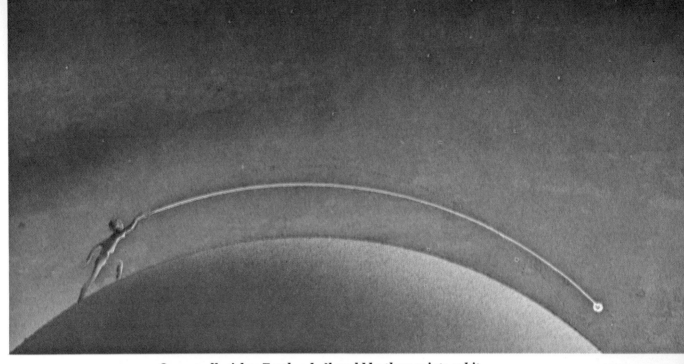

On a small, airless Earth, a ball could be thrown into orbit

In the second place, the Earth would have to be a very small body—say about ten miles wide. On the real Earth your ball will not go around because it keeps falling until it hits the ground. But on the little imaginary Earth, the ground curves away exactly as much as your ball falls. So the ball keeps falling but never hits the ground. Instead, it falls *around* the Earth. It is in orbit.

An artificial satellite stays in orbit in the same way. In the first place, its path is high enough to be above the Earth's air. At such a height the force of gravity will pull it down 16 feet a second. To stay up, it must fall only as much as the Earth's surface curves. The curvature is 16 feet in 5 miles. Since the satellite falls 16 feet a second, it must travel 5 miles in that second. Then it falls 16 feet in 5 miles, which is as much as the Earth's surface curves. So the satellite falls around the Earth, in orbit.

In a higher orbit the rate of fall will be less. At a height of 239,000 miles, a satellite will fall only about 1/19 of an inch a second. To stay in orbit, it has to travel only about 2/3 of a mile a second.

It happens that there really is a satellite in such an orbit, traveling at this speed. You know the satellite very well. It is the Earth's natural satellite, the Moon.

A satellite is a falling body. Because of its forward speed it falls around the Earth

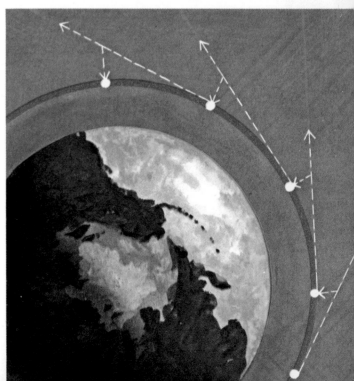

17

Orange and red colors appear in the sky when the Sun is low

THE ATMOSPHERE

Around the Earth lies a shell of air—the atmosphere. It is just as much a part of the planet as the land and sea beneath it. The air is a mixture of several gases, which are very important for us and other living creatures. Animals must breathe oxygen from the air to stay alive. Plants must take carbon dioxide from it to grow. Bacteria in the soil take nitrogen from the air and make compounds needed by plants and animals.

The lower air is dense, with gas molecules closer together than at upper levels

upper atmosphere

gas molecules

aurora

lower atmosphere

The gases are made up of invisible particles called molecules. Each gas is a certain kind of molecule. Of every 10,000 molecules in the air, 7,809 are nitrogen; 2,095 are oxygen; 93 are a gas called argon; and 3 are carbon dioxide.

The molecules are always in motion, darting about in all directions. This keeps the four gases well mixed, so air has about the same make-up everywhere around the Earth.

The air at lower levels also contains water. Most of it is in the form of the invisible gas, water vapor. When air cools off, water vapor molecules collect into droplets or tiny ice crystals. When droplets and crystals become very numerous, they form clouds.

A Protecting Shield

A few speedy gas particles at the top of the atmosphere escape into space. The rest are held by gravity. The weight of overlying layers of atmosphere presses on the air beneath, crowding its molecules together. Thus the lower air is

18

thickest—most *dense*. About nine-tenths of all the matter in the atmosphere is packed into the first ten miles above the Earth. Above that, particles are farther and farther apart. A hundred miles up, the atmosphere is so thin that a satellite can pass through safely. Much higher than that, the atmosphere fades away into space.

Filmy as it is, the atmosphere shields us from certain dangers. Among these are meteorites—bits of solid matter that rush in from space. You have probably seen them streaking across the sky as "shooting stars," or meteors. Only a few are bright enough to be noticed, but countless numbers shower down during the night, and also in daytime.

Once in a while a large meteorite falls right through the atmosphere and lands as a chunk of rock or metal. But most do not reach the Earth's surface. Usually, a meteorite is destroyed while still high up. Friction with the atmosphere makes it so hot that it turns into glowing vapor.

If a satellite's orbit dips too low into the atmosphere, the satellite will heat up in the same way, vaporize, and become a meteor.

Why the Sky is Blue

Sunlight has blue and all the other colors of the rainbow hidden in it. This can be shown by passing a beam of sunlight through a prism. The white light becomes separated into red, orange, yellow, green, blue, and violet. This series of colors is the spectrum. Each color is bent in passing through the prism, but some are bent more than others, so they come out in different places.

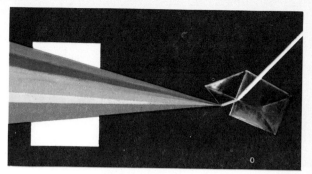
A prism separates sunlight into rainbow colors

Light travels in waves. The waves are of different lengths, with the shortest at the blue and violet end of the spectrum. These wave lengths are scattered more than others in bumping against molecules of air. As a result, the scattered blue light gives its color to the sky.

Around the Sun at sunrise and sunset, the sky is usually pink, with little or no blue. Why? Because of the Sun's low position, the light travels a long way through the lower atmosphere. Much of the blue is stopped by air molecules and other particles. More of the red light is left, coloring the sky with lovely shades of pink and rose.

The blue of sunlight is scattered by air particles

19

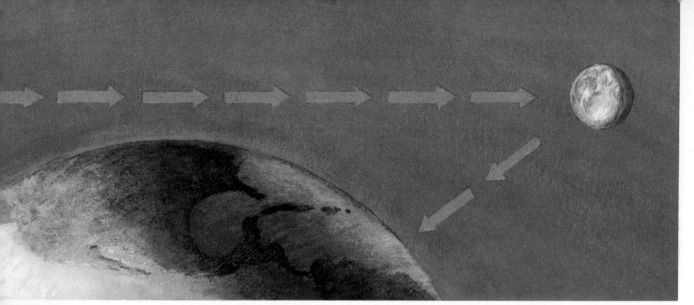

Sunlight falls on the Moon and is reflected to the Earth as moonlight

THE MOON

The Moon is the Earth's smaller companion in space. Its diameter—the width through its center—is a little more than one-fourth the Earth's diameter.

You can observe the Moon very easily. It is brightly lighted by sunlight, and is never hidden by any clouds of its own. If you see the Moon disappear behind clouds, they are the Earth's clouds. On the Moon there is no moisture to make clouds. And there is no air that clouds might float in. That is because gravity on the Moon is only about one-sixth as strong as on the Earth. It is too weak to hold gases.

Just by glancing at the Moon, you notice that its surface is marked with lighter and darker patches. Through a small telescope or field glasses you can see what sort of things the markings are. You see wide, flat expanses that are darker than the rest of the surface. These are called *maria,* meaning seas, because early observers supposed they were bodies of water. Now we know they are plains, probably made of dark rock.

In other places are chains of mountains. When sunlight strikes the mountains on one side, that side is bright while the other is in deep shadow. Among the mountains, and also around the plains, are many circular hollows—craters. There are large and small craters, in groups and single, and each is ringed with a rocky ridge.

The Moon's Phases

The Moon, like the Sun and stars, rises in the east and sets in the west. Of course, this daily rising and setting is caused by the Earth's rotation.

But the Moon also has its own real motion, circling the Earth in about four weeks. It moves in the same direction as the Earth rotates—toward the east. You can detect this motion by watching the Moon rise day after day.

Say you time the moonrise on a certain day, and it is 8:00 P. M. A day later at the same time, the Earth has made a full turn. The observation point where you watched the first moonrise is back to its former position, but where is the Moon?

It has gone ahead, and you will not see it until about 50 minutes later, when your observation point has caught up with the Moon. Two weeks later the Moon will not be seen in the night sky at all. It will rise in the morning and set in the evening.

During its trip the Moon appears to change shape. As astronomers say, it goes through phases. The phases are due to the way in which we see the Moon in different positions along its orbit. At the point where it lies between us and the Sun, the side of the Moon facing us is dark, so we do not see the Moon at all. This phase is called new Moon.

When the Moon has moved a little farther along, we can see a small part of the lighted side. This appears as a thin crescent. By the time the Moon has gone a quarter of the way around, we see half the lighted side. This phase is called the first quarter.

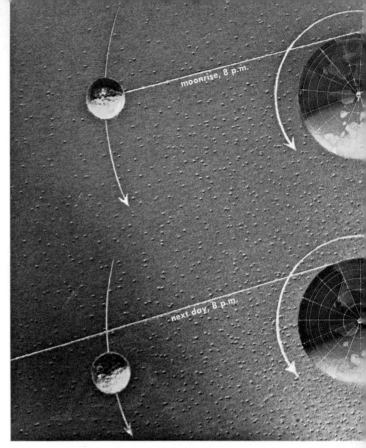

Because of the Moon's motion in its orbit, moonrise comes 50 minutes later each day

When the Moon has gone half way around its orbit, all of the sunlit side is facing us, so we see the Moon full and round. This phase is called full Moon.

As the Moon swings around toward the Sun, we see less and less of the sunlit side. Finally the Moon is back between us and the Sun again, and disappears.

When the Moon is a crescent, observe it carefully after sunset. The dark part can be seen faintly. It is dim because the light by which we see it is sunlight that has been reflected twice. The light is reflected from the Earth to the Moon, then from the Moon back to us again.

We always see only one side of the Moon—never the "back" of it. That is because the Moon makes a full turn in the same time it takes to circle the Earth. Thus the same side is always turned toward us.

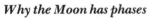

Why the Moon has phases

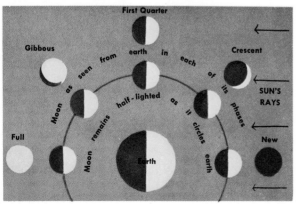

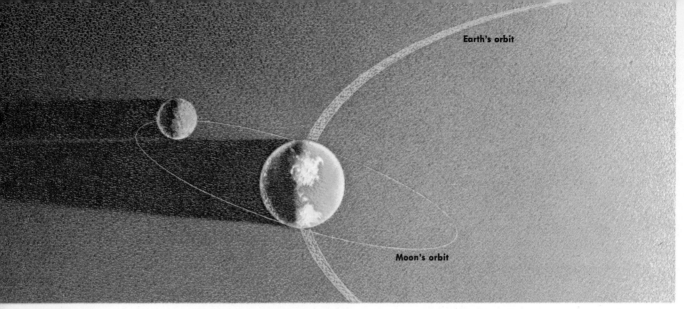

The Moon's orbit is tilted to the plane of the Earth's orbit

ECLIPSES

Sometimes, when the Moon is full, a shadow creeps across its face and covers it for an hour or more. Then the shadow slowly moves away and the Moon is bright again.

Such a darkening is a lunar eclipse—an eclipse of the Moon. Greek astronomers of long ago recognized it as the Earth's shadow crossing the Moon. They noticed that the edge of the shadow is always curved, and guessed from this that the Earth is round.

Eclipses of the Moon

It is easy to see why lunar eclipses happen at full Moon. That is the time when the Earth is between the Sun and Moon. Earth's shadow, reaching far out into space, falls right across the Moon's path.

Why is there not an eclipse at every full Moon? This would happen if the Moon's orbit were on the same plane as the Earth's. But the Moon's orbit is tipped a little compared to the Earth's. Because of this, the Moon usually passes above or beneath the Earth's shadow. Only once in a while does it pass through the shadow. Sometimes only part of the Moon enters the shadow,

Lunar eclipse: the Moon in the Earth's shadow

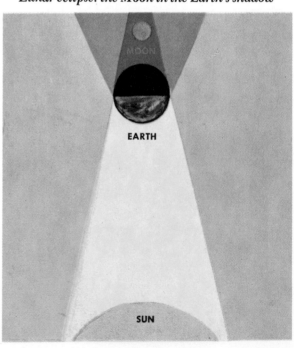

22

making a partial eclipse instead of a total one.

During an eclipse, the shadowed part of the Moon is not absolutely dark. It can be seen in a faint reddish light. This is sunrise and sunset color, caused by light that has passed through the Earth's lower atmosphere.

Astronomers observe an eclipse of the Sun

Eclipses of the Sun

Sometimes the Moon comes exactly between the Earth and the Sun, causing an eclipse of the Sun. A solar eclipse is exciting to watch, but dangerous. Looking directly at the Sun can injure your eyes. It is safe only if you screen the light by looking through very dark glass, or through several dark film negatives. Or you can watch the eclipse on TV.

The eclipse begins when the Moon conceals a little strip on one side of the Sun. Then it creeps farther and farther across the Sun. If the eclipse is total, the Moon covers the Sun completely for a while, then moves on. At the moment when the Sun is entirely hidden, sky and Earth become dark. Stars appear. Around the black disk of the Moon, a pearly halo glows. This is the Sun's corona, or atmosphere.

A solar eclipse can be seen only along a narrow path across the Earth. That is because the Moon is not wide enough to block our line of sight with the Sun from everywhere on Earth.

During a partial eclipse, the Moon does not completely cover the Sun, and the sky does not become dark enough for the Sun's corona to show.

The Moon is not always exactly at the same distance from the Earth, because its orbit is not exactly a circle. When farther away than usual, the Moon may pass squarely across the Sun and still not completely cover it. Then the edge of the Sun shows all around the Moon as a bright ring. This is called an annular or ring eclipse.

Each year there are between two and five solar eclipses. Astronomers can predict them because they understand exactly how the Moon and Earth move in relation to the Sun.

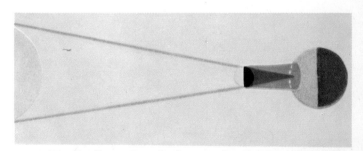

Total eclipse: deep shadow reaches Earth

Annular eclipse: deep shadow does not reach Earth

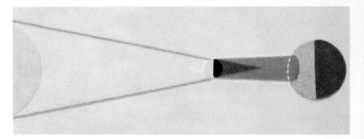

Between one moonrise and the next, there are two high and two low tides

THE TIDES

Have you ever watched the tide come in? Hour after hour the ocean rises along the shore, creeping up beaches, pouring through inlets, filling harbors and river mouths. The tide reaches high-water mark and pauses there a while. This is high tide. Then the ebb or falling tide begins. After several hours, the water is at its lowest level. This is low tide.

A tide is a bulging of the ocean. The bulge moves from east to west like an enormous wave. Meanwhile, another bulge is moving in the same direction on the opposite side of the Earth. Where continents lie in the way, the tides are stopped. But where the ocean is open they go on traveling around the world.

The round trip of a tidal bulge takes about 24 hours and 50 minutes. This period is the time from one moonrise to the next.

For centuries, people wondered why the tides keep pace with the Moon. Isaac Newton found the answer. He realized that the tides are caused by the gravitational pull of the Moon and Sun on the ocean waters. Because the Moon is nearer, its influence is greater.

As the Earth's turning surface passes under the Moon, the pull of gravitation between Earth and Moon works upon the ocean. It raises the water in a bulge, which follows the Moon around the Earth. On the opposite side of the world, where the Moon's attraction is weaker, the water lags away from the Earth a little and forms another bulge. In regions between the two bulges, the waters are at low tide.

The Sun also takes part in the tug-of-war. At new Moon, the Sun and Moon are in line on the same side of the Earth. The Sun's pull is added to the Moon's, and this makes an unusually high tide —a spring tide. There is another spring tide at full Moon, when Sun and Moon are in line again, but on opposite sides of the Earth.

At the quarters, the position of the Moon is crosswise to the line between Sun and Earth. The Moon pulls one way, the Sun another. The Sun's pull works against the Moon's, causing a small tide—a neap tide.

The pull of Moon and Sun works on the Earth's atmosphere as well as on the ocean. Turning with the rest of the planet, the atmosphere passes under the Moon and is drawn out in a vast bulge. This is an atmospheric tide. It moves around the Earth in time with the Moon, while another bulge moves around on the planet's opposite side.

Even the land and rock of the Earth are pulled out of shape by the attraction of Moon and Sun. Scientists have made careful measurements, and have found that the land surface rises and falls several inches every day. These movements are tides in the solid Earth.

The Slowing of Rotation

The Moon's attraction pulls on the tidal bulges and tends to hold them back. After millions of years of this dragging effect, the Earth's rotation has been slowed. Long ago it was faster than now, and the day was shorter. In the future, rotation will continue slowing down, and the day will very gradually become longer.

The Moon also has tidal bulges, caused mainly by the Earth's pull. Long ago the Moon probably rotated fast enough to have a day as long as ours. Gradually, the Earth's drag on the bulges slowed down the Moon's rotation until it no longer turned different sides toward the Earth.

Isaac Newton, who discovered the law of gravitation, found that the pull of Moon and Sun causes the tides

Spring tide: Earth, Moon and Sun are in line. Neap tide: Moon is crosswise to a line from Earth to Sun

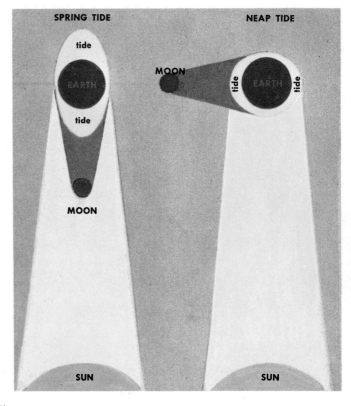

25

IN ORBIT AROUND THE SUN

Our planet Earth is a satellite of the Sun. It circles the Sun in a great orbit nearly 600 million miles around, travels more than a million miles a day, and completes a round trip in just a year. What a marvelous space ship! The Earth rushes us along at a speed of over 66 thousand miles an hour, but the motion is so smooth that we do not feel it at all.

The pull of gravitation between Sun and Earth is much greater than the pull between Earth and Moon. This is be-

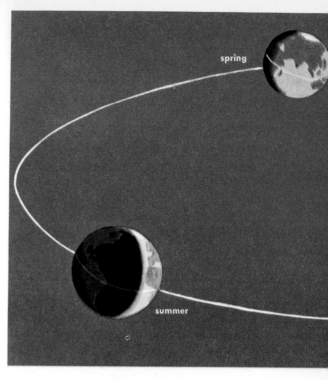

As the Earth travels around the Sun, its tilt causes the seasons

The boy holds the whirling stone in orbit

cause the Sun is an enormous body containing a great amount of matter. It has enough material to make 334,000 planets like the Earth.

In scientific language, the amount of matter in a body is called its *mass*. This is very important, for the mass of two bodies, as well as their distance, determines the attraction between them.

Sun and Earth are about 93 million miles apart—much farther apart than Earth and Moon. But the Sun's mass times the Earth's mass causes a much greater pull than the Earth's mass times the Moon's. If such a force were to be held by a steel cable, the cable would have to be a few thousand miles thick. Gravitation is always at work, pulling the Earth toward the Sun. But the Earth's speed in orbit keeps it from falling into the Sun, and it falls around instead.

26

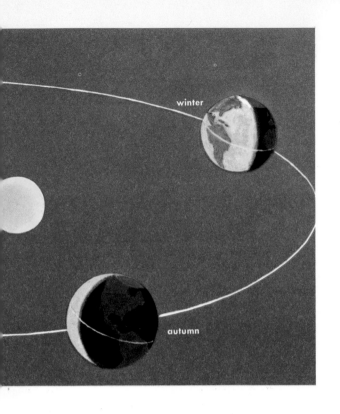

By June 21 the Earth has gone half-way around its orbit. The North Pole is now tilted toward the Sun, and sunlight reaches the Pole and the region around it. All over the northern hemisphere, days are long, nights are short.

By September 21, day and night are equal, as they were on March 21. As the Earth passes this position, the northern hemisphere tilts away from the Sun, making nights there longer.

When the Earth has come all the way around to its position of December 21, the north is tilted farthest away from the Sun. The yearly trip is over and another begins. But there is no real beginning nor end to this journey. The Earth goes on revolving around the Sun, as it has done for thousands of millions of years.

Yearly Round Trip

Imagine you are far out in space, where you can see the Earth's entire orbit and watch what happens during its yearly trip around the Sun. You begin to watch on December 21, which is the first day of winter in the northern hemisphere.

You observe that the Earth is tilted—its axis is at a slant to its orbit. At this time of year the North Pole is pointed away from the Sun. Daylight—sunlight—does not reach the Pole nor the region around it. Farther south in the northern hemisphere there is some daylight, but days are short and nights are long.

The tilt of the axis stays the same as the Earth moves along in its orbit. By March 21 it has gone a quarter of the way around. Now neither pole is tilted away from the Sun. Both receive sunlight. Between the polar regions, every place is turned toward the Sun for 12 hours and away from it for 12.

The Sun holds the Earth in orbit

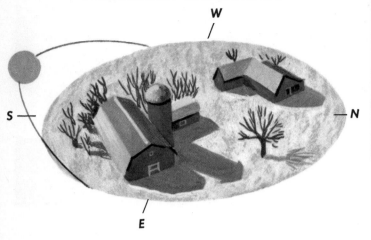

In winter the Sun's daily path is low

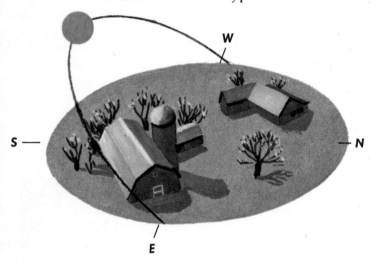

In spring and autumn the Sun's path is higher

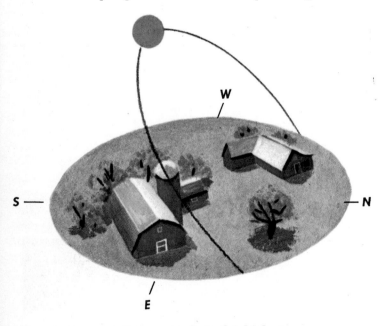

In summer, its path is highest

Summer night in the Arctic...

THE SEASONS

During our northern winter, all the trees except the evergreens are bare of leaves. Small animals have burrowed underground to escape the cold. Summer birds have flown south.

The Sun rises late, takes a low course across the sky, and sets early. Air, ground, and water do not become as warm as they do in summer, since there are fewer hours of sunshine each day. Also, sunrays strike the Earth's surface at a slant, and as a result fewer rays fall in a given area.

Days are short and sunrays are slanting because the northern hemisphere is tilted away from the Sun. In the far North the Sun has disappeared altogether, and people must live through weeks of darkness. Meanwhile, the southern hemisphere is tilted toward the Sun, and is having its summer.

A few months later, springtime comes in the northern hemisphere. Days are longer and warmer. Buds burst open; birds return. Soon the hemisphere is tilted toward the Sun, and summer begins. The Sun rises early, climbs high in the sky, and sets late. Its path from

...the Sun at 20-minute intervals

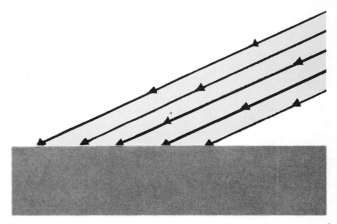

Slanting rays spread over a wide area

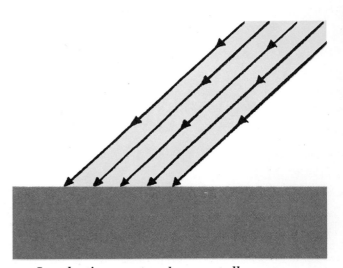

Less slanting rays spread over a smaller area

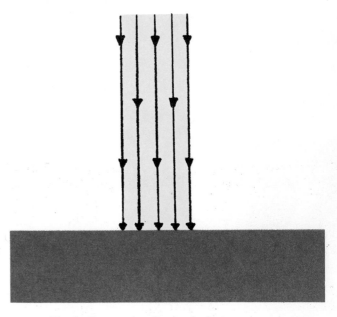

Vertical rays spread over the least area

sunrise to sunset is longer than at any other time of year, giving us more than 12 hours of daylight. Sunrays now are nearly straight up-and-down, so that more fall in a given area. Because of the longer day and more concentrated sunlight, the weather is warm.

In the far North, the Sun does not set all summer long, but remains shining even at midnight. Every 24 hours, while the Earth makes a full turn, the Sun circles the sky near the horizon.

In autumn, days become shorter again, and the Sun's rays slant more and more. The air is chilled. Trees lose their leaves, birds fly south, and we get ready for winter.

Imagine what the world would be like if the Earth's axis were not tilted. At both poles the Sun would be seen circling the horizon all year long. It would never set. Everywhere else, day and night would always be equal, just as they are now at the beginning of spring and autumn. The polar regions would be cold and the zones between would be warm, but at any one place the weather would always be about the same. The Earth would go on circling the Sun, but it would surely be a duller world, since it would have no seasons.

29

The Incas measured the year from a shadow

MEASURING THE YEAR

To know what day it is, we just look at the calendar. This seems simple enough, but if you think about it, the calendar is really quite a remarkable thing.

The calendar was unknown among people who lived by hunting and gathering wild food. To them, it did not matter when one year ended and another began. Even in recent times, hunting people did not keep track of the year.

But when people began to live by farming, they had to pay more attention to time. They had to know when the

Dawn of the first day of summer at Stonehenge

seasons came, and when to plant and harvest their crops.

One way to measure the year is by observing the Sun. This was the method of the Incas of the Andes Mountains, in South America. As their measuring instrument, the Incas used a stone pillar to cast a shadow. They marked where the shadow fell at noon at different seasons. At the beginning of summer, when the Sun reaches its highest position, the shadow was shortest. At the beginning of winter, when the Sun is lowest in the sky, the shadow was longest. The time between one day of shortest shadow and the next was exactly a year.

People of ancient England used gateways of rock to sight the rising Sun at various times of the year. A circle of such gateways, called Stonehenge, or "hanging stones," stands to this day on Salisbury Plain. One gate frames the rising Sun on the first day of summer.

A Star Marks the Year

Some ancient peoples measured the year by observing a star. You, too, can do this. For your observatory, use a window that faces either east or west. Select a star near the window frame. Line it up with some neighbor's TV antenna or chimney. Stick a pin in the window frame so that pin, antenna and star are all in line. Write down the day, hour, and minute when you line up the star. On the following day at the same time, observe the star and you will find it slightly out of line. Watch it day after day at the same time. It will get more and more out of line.

Remember that the Earth is always

moving along in its orbit. Because of this, your side of the Earth faces in a slightly different direction every day, causing apparent shifts of the star. After a certain time the star disappears—it is hidden behind the Earth during the hours of darkness. But nearly a year after you began your observations, you will find the star back in the sky and getting into line again. When it is exactly in line, a year has passed. The Earth has come back to the position from which you first sighted the star.

In ancient Egypt, the year was measured by watching Sirius, the Dog Star, brightest of all the stars. For seventy nights Sirius was absent from the sky. Then, just before sunrise on a certain day in June, the star reappeared over the eastern horizon.

This was a very important time. Egypt had almost no rainfall, and the people depended on the Nile River, as they do today, for the water needed to irrigate their fields. The river rose and flooded every year at the time of the return of Sirius.

Priests of the temples watched for the star's return. A certain temple faced the direction where Sirius would appear. An aisle of columns led to the statue of a goddess. The statue's eyes were jewels. When Sirius appeared, its light fell on the jewels. At this signal, the priests marched from the temple and announced the new year—the time to open the irrigation canals.

Today, astronomers still keep track of time by observing the Sun and the stars. With their fine precision instruments they measure the year down to a fraction of a second.

Lining up a star

The star's position two weeks later

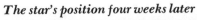

The star's position four weeks later

31

Armillary sphere used in ancient China to show the positions of Sun, Moon, and planets

STORY OF THE CALENDAR

Very long ago, before the year was measured and the calendar invented, people kept time by the Moon. They would say that a certain event had happened "three moons ago." A "moon" was a lunar month—the period between one new Moon and the next. In those days the word "month" meant "Moon."

People did not celebrate birthdays, since they had no year. And they did not remember their age in months, but just remembered that they had been born after certain persons and before others.

The lunar month lasts 29 days, 12 hours, 44 minutes and a few seconds. It cannot be divided evenly into weeks.

Nevertheless, ancient peoples did divide the lunar month roughly into half-months, and the half-month into weeks of unequal length. Later, a standard month of 30 or 31 days was adopted, and also a week of seven days. You can tell from the names of the days that time keeping was done by people who studied the heavens. Sunday is the Sun's day, Monday is the Moon's day, and Saturday is Saturn's day.

Fitting Months into the Year

The year—the period of the Earth's trip around the Sun—lasts 365 days, 5 hours, 48 minutes and 46 seconds. Try fitting months into that period!

The ancient Romans at one time divided their year into 12 lunar months. This made the year too short, so an extra month was added when necessary. For several years the priests in charge of calendar keeping neglected to add months, and as a result the calendar fell behind the seasons by about 80 days.

To end this confusion, Julius Caesar called upon a Greek astronomer for help, and the astronomer, Sosigenes, devised a new calendar.

The months were made either 30 or 31 days long, except February, which was given 29 days. Every fourth year was made a leap year, with an extra day added to February.

Julius Caesar named one of the 31-day months July, after himself. The next ruler, Augustus, named the following month August, in honor of himself. Legend says that August had originally been a 30-day month, and that Augustus stole a day from February to make his month as long as July. Thus February became a 28-day month except in leap year, when it had 29 days.

Calendar Reform

The Julian calendar—the calendar of Julius Caesar—worked fairly well and was adopted in many countries. But it was based on a year 11 minutes and 14 seconds too long. With the passing of centuries this error began to cause trouble. By the year 1582 the calendar was ten days behind the seasons. Scientists proved this to Pope Gregory XIII. He ordered a correction, and October 5, 1582, was made October 15, 1582.

To prevent the same problem from coming up again, a new rule was made. Every four centuries, three leap year days would be dropped.

The corrected calendar, known as the Gregorian calendar, was not adopted by the American colonies until 1752. By then the old calendar was 11 days behind the new one. When the change was made, it seemed to some people that 11 days had been "lost," and were taken away from their age.

To keep the record straight, they moved their birthdays ahead 11 days. George Washington, for example, whose birthday was on February 11 by the old calendar, shifted it to February 22, the date that is celebrated today.

Our present calendar serves us fairly well, but there are many ways in which it could be improved. As it is, the quarters of the year do not start at the beginnings of months; months do not begin on any set day of the week; and many holidays do not fall on the same day of the week each year. It would be convenient to have the quarters of the year always start at the beginnings of months, and holidays always fall on the same day of the week. Calendars with these and other improvements have been worked out. One of them is called the World Calendar. Perhaps it will be adopted some day by all nations.

A proposed World Calendar

FIRST QUARTER		
JANUARY	**FEBRUARY**	**MARCH**
S M T W T F S	S M T W T F S	S M T W T F S
1 2 3 4 5 6 7	1 2 3 4	1 2
8 9 10 11 12 13 14	5 6 7 8 9 10 11	3 4 5 6 7 8 9
15 16 17 18 19 20 21	12 13 14 15 16 17 18	10 11 12 13 14 15 16
22 23 24 25 26 27 28	19 20 21 22 23 24 25	17 18 19 20 21 22 23
29 30 31	26 27 28 29 30	24 25 26 27 28 29 30

SECOND QUARTER		
APRIL	**MAY**	**JUNE**
S M T W T F S	S M T W T F S	S M T W T F S
1 2 3 4 5 6 7	1 2 3 4	1 2
8 9 10 11 12 13 14	5 6 7 8 9 10 11	3 4 5 6 7 8 9
15 16 17 18 19 20 21	12 13 14 15 16 17 18	10 11 12 13 14 15 16
22 23 24 25 26 27 28	19 20 21 22 23 24 25	17 18 19 20 21 22 23
29 30 31	26 27 28 29 30	24 25 26 27 28 29 30 W

THIRD QUARTER		
JULY	**AUGUST**	**SEPTEMBER**
S M T W T F S	S M T W T F S	S M T W T F S
1 2 3 4 5 6 7	1 2 3 4	1 2
8 9 10 11 12 13 14	5 6 7 8 9 10 11	3 4 5 6 7 8 9
15 16 17 18 19 20 21	12 13 14 15 16 17 18	10 11 12 13 14 15 16
22 23 24 25 26 27 28	19 20 21 22 23 24 25	17 18 19 20 21 22 23
29 30 31	26 27 28 29 30	24 25 26 27 28 29 30

FOURTH QUARTER		
OCTOBER	**NOVEMBER**	**DECEMBER**
S M T W T F S	S M T W T F S	S M T W T F S
1 2 3 4 5 6 7	1 2 3 4	1 2
8 9 10 11 12 13 14	5 6 7 8 9 10 11	3 4 5 6 7 8 9
15 16 17 18 19 20 21	12 13 14 15 16 17 18	10 11 12 13 14 15 16
22 23 24 25 26 27 28	19 20 21 22 23 24 25	17 18 19 20 21 22 23
29 30 31	26 27 28 29 30	24 25 26 27 28 29 30 W

Worldsday (a World Holiday), W or December 31 (365th day), follows December 30 every year.
The Leapyear Day (another World Holiday), W or June 31, follows June 30 in leap years only.

Lippershey making the first telescope

THE TELESCOPE

Around the year 1600, a Dutch maker of eyeglasses, Hans Lippershey, discovered a way to see farther than any man had ever seen before. He held two lenses a certain distance apart, looked through them, and found that distant objects appeared large and clear. Then, setting the two lenses in a tube, Lippershey made a telescope.

At first the telescope was used as a "spyglass" to watch such things as ships and enemy soldiers. But when news of the instrument reached Galileo in Italy, he decided to have one for studying the heavens.

Galileo made himself a telescope and trained it on the Moon. He saw mountains as great as those on the Earth, showing that the Moon was a world. Then he looked at the mysterious bodies called planets, which means wanderers. To the unaided eye, the planets appear as points of light, like stars. Only one difference is easy to see—they slowly shift position, moving against the background of the stars.

Through his telescope, Galileo saw that Jupiter and the other planets no longer appeared as points of light. They were disks, like the Moon. They were worlds!

Light and Seeing

Today, several kinds of telescopes are used in astronomical observatories. One kind is like Galileo's, with a lens at one end of the tube and an eyepiece at the other.

This telescope resembles our eye, which also has a lens built into it. The lens serves to collect light, and thus form an image or picture of objects.

If a heavenly body is far away and dim, we can see it better only by collecting more light from it. This is the purpose of the telescope. The large lens collects much more light than our eye.

When the telescope is trained on a distant body, light rays from the body come through the lens and in passing through it are bent inward—refracted. This brings them together at a point near the other end of the tube, where they form a little image. The observer looks at this image through the eyepiece, which magnifies it.

The largest refracting telescope is at the Yerkes Observatory, in Wisconsin. Its main lens is 40 inches across and is set in a tube over 60 feet long. This is about as big as a refracting telescope can be. A larger lens would be hard to mount, since it is supported only around its edge. Any support crossing behind it would block the light.

34

In another kind of telescope, a curved mirror collects the light. The rays enter the open end of the tube and fall on a mirror, which is mounted at the closed end. The rays are reflected from the curved mirror to a small flat mirror near the open end of the tube. An image is formed on the small mirror and reflected into the eyepiece.

A reflecting telescope can be much larger than a refractor, since the mirror is supported from behind as well as around the edge. The largest telescope in use so far is the giant Hale reflector on Mount Palomar, in California. Its mirror, which is 200 inches across, collects 640,000 times more light than the human eye.

Large telescopes are used mainly with cameras to photograph the sky. If the film is exposed for a long time, it may record an image of some object too dim to be seen by an observer looking through the eyepiece.

To keep the instrument aimed at one point while the Earth turns, a motor slowly guides it. Thus the great eye of the telescope follows the stars.

The 40-inch refracting telescope at Yerkes Observatory in Wisconsin

The radio telescope picks up broadcasts from unseen bodies in space

SIGNALS FROM THE STARS

Astronomers learn a lot about the stars by analyzing their light. For this purpose they use an instrument called the spectroscope, which is placed at the eyepiece of a telescope.

Starlight enters the spectroscope through a narrow slit, then goes through a prism which divides it into the colors of the spectrum. The colored light passes through a small telescope and is projected on a screen. A camera may be attached to the small telescope to photograph the spectrum. Then the instrument is called a spectrograph.

Originally, the spectroscope was an instrument of the chemistry laboratory. Chemists still use it to identify substances and find out what they are made of. They heat a sample of a substance until it glows, pass its light through the spectroscope, and look for certain lines crossing the spectrum. The number and position of these lines tell what substance caused them.

Astronomers analyze starlight in a similar way. When they find certain lines crossing a star's spectrum, they can identify substances that exist on the star.

Another instrument, the photometer, measures the brightness of stars. In the kind of photometer most used today, starlight is beamed to a photoelectric cell and sets up an electric current. The amount of current shows the strength or brightness of the light. An instrument called the bolometer is used to measure the heat radiating from a star.

The spectroscope identifies a star's elements

slit

prism

spectrum

Tuning In on the Stars

Light travels as waves of energy. The waves have different lengths, measured in hundred-thousandths of an inch. Wave lengths toward the red end of the spectrum are longer; those toward the violet end are shorter.

All the wave lengths from red to violet are visible. The eye, telescope, and camera are the instruments for receiving them. But there are certain other kinds of waves which cannot be seen. Among them are radio waves, which are much longer than light waves, and X rays, which are much shorter. Both go out from the Sun and stars. Optical or "seeing" instruments are useless to detect them. Other kinds are needed.

Special receivers called radio telescopes are used in listening to radio emissions from the Sun and stars. One type has an antenna shaped like a giant saucer. Occasionally it picks up signals from an unknown source. Then astronomers aim their telescopes and cameras in the direction of the source. And sometimes they get a picture of an object that has never been seen before.

View from above the Atmosphere

Astronomers are always trying to see farther into space. You might think they would want much larger telescopes than the Hale reflector. But they know that there are practical limits to the size of telescopes. For one thing, the larger an instrument, the more it magnifies disturbances caused by the air.

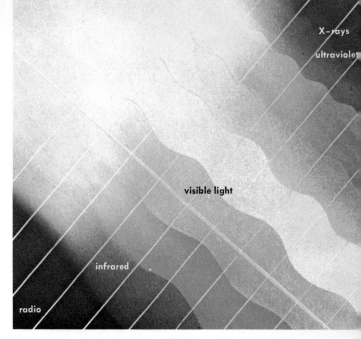

Energy waves of different lengths

The trouble is not with the telescopes, but with the Earth's atmosphere. Starlight is bent this way and that in coming through layers of air of different density. This zigzag course of the light makes the stars seem to twinkle. It makes any image waver, or shimmer, and the wavering is magnified by a large telescope. As a result, a picture taken through it is fuzzy.

When an astronaut sees the stars from above the atmosphere, they do not twinkle. They shine with a steady light. Astronomers want the astronaut's view. They want to lift telescopes above the atmosphere and get clear, sharp images.

Telescopes and cameras have already been sent up in balloons to take pictures from above the thicker part of the atmosphere. They have also been launched in satellites. The next step will be to place telescopes on the Moon.

Then astronomers will no longer have to look through the Earth's distorting atmosphere. They will look through space and receive clear, unwavering light from the stars.

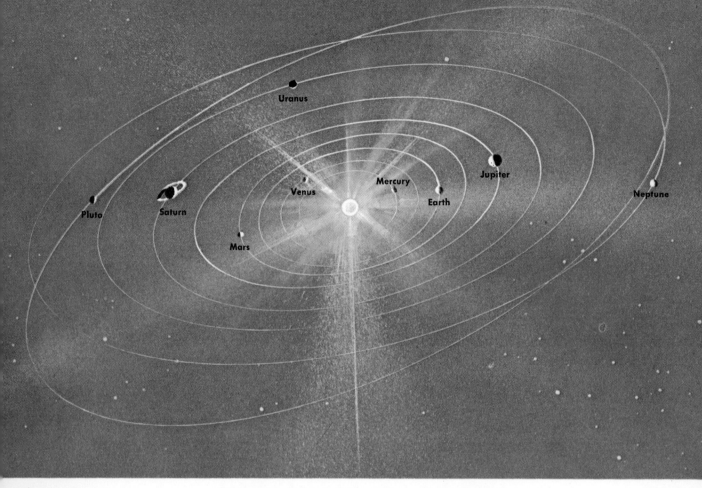

The orbits of the nine planets lie nearly in one plane

PART TWO

Kingdom of the Sun

THE SOLAR SYSTEM

The Earth belongs to a family of nine worlds—nine planets circling the Sun. Six of the worlds have moons revolving around them while they revolve around the Sun. In addition, there is a swarm of dwarf planets—asteroids—most of which travel in a belt beyond the orbit of Mars.

The Sun's attraction holds all these whirling bodies together in a system that runs on and on, according to the laws of motion and gravitation.

The worlds all move around the Sun in the same direction. Their orbits are tilted a bit in relation to one another, but the tilt is so small that the orbits lie nearly in one plane. If we could view the solar system from a distant point in space, it would look almost flat.

Even with the view we have from the Earth, we can recognize the flat shape of the system. Suppose we observe the Sun's apparent motion during a year. We see that the Sun takes an eastward path around the sky. This path is called the ecliptic. Of course, it is really due to the Earth's orbital motion.

When we observe the paths of the planets and the Moon, we notice that they lie near the Sun's path. This shows their orbits are almost on one plane.

Orbital Speeds and Distances

Each planet moves at its own speed. The speed depends on the distance of the orbit from the Sun. A nearer planet moves faster; a more distant one moves slower. Mercury, the nearest planet, must travel 30 miles a second to stay in its orbit. It completes a round trip in less than 3 months. Pluto, in the most distant orbit, travels about 3 miles a second. Its round trip—its year—lasts 248 of our years.

The planets in the orbits nearest ours—Mercury, Venus, Mars, Jupiter, and Saturn—reflect enough sunlight to be seen with the unaided eye. Only these five planets were known before the invention of the telescope. They were named after ancient gods, so when the three more distant planets were discovered, they too were given names of gods—Uranus, Neptune, and Pluto.

Since an inner planet makes its trip in a shorter time than outer planets, it gradually overtakes them in the procession around the sky. Thus the Earth passes Mars, and for a while it seems to us that Mars is slipping backward.

At a certain time, two or more planets may appear close together. Several months later only one is in the visible half of the sky, or perhaps none is there. But wherever they are in their orbits, our companion worlds keep close to the path of the Sun and the Moon.

Moon and planets in their paths across the sky

Close-up view of the Sun showing its stormy surface

OUR STAR, THE SUN

The Sun was once thought to be a great fire blazing in the sky. But a fire soon uses up its fuel and burns out, whereas the Sun has been glowing and pouring forth energy for several thousand million years.

The Sun is not a fire; it is a star. If it were many million million miles from the Earth, the Sun would look like any other star. It appears larger and brighter simply because it is much nearer—only 93 million miles away.

What is a Star?

Hydrogen atoms (H) fuse and form helium (He)

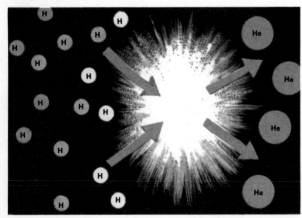

Scientists began to understand the nature of the Sun when they analyzed its light with the spectroscope. The spectrum shows that the Sun is made of the

40

same sort of matter as the Earth. Its elements—the various kinds of atoms—are those that also form the Earth's rock, water, and air.

On the Sun, however, the atoms do not form solids or liquids. Temperatures are too high—thousands of degrees on the surface, millions in the interior. At such temperatures, all substances are gases, with the atoms rushing about and mixing. On the Sun, even copper, iron, silver and gold are gases.

Discoveries from Photographs

Astronomers take pictures of the Sun through filters. A filter strains out most of the wave lengths of light, letting only certain ones through. For example, one filter lets through wave lengths from the part of the spectrum where the line of the element hydrogen is found. When this filter is used, we say the picture is taken in hydrogen light. Astronomers select a light that shows most clearly the features which they wish to study.

Some photographs reveal that the Sun's surface is covered with bright flecks—granules—encircled by darker material. The granules are bubbles of hot gas hundreds of miles across. They burst from the Sun's interior, last a few minutes, and are replaced by others. The material around the granules is cooler gas sinking back into the Sun. It is really bright, but appears dark by comparison with the granules.

Sunspots

Three and a half centuries ago Galileo and another observer discovered that the Sun's surface often becomes marked with dark spots. They first appear as a group of small spots, which grow and merge into a few large ones. These may spread over an area several times wider than the Earth. After a few weeks they shrink and disappear, and another group forms.

Galileo observed that the spots move slowly across the face of the Sun. Sometimes a group disappears on one edge of the Sun and about two weeks later reappears on the opposite edge. From this Galileo saw that the Sun rotates, turning in the same direction as the Earth.

Astronomers have timed the rotation of the spots and learned that the Sun's

The Sun's rotation is shown by shifting of the position of sunspots

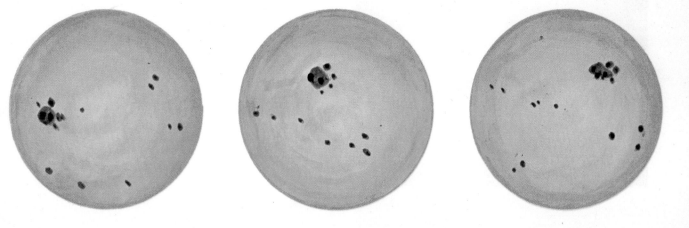

equatorial zone makes a full turn in about 25 days. The polar zones rotate in 33 days. This shows that the Sun is not a solid body, with all the parts fixed and moving together. It is a whirling sphere of gases.

Sunspots are caused by disturbances which dam up the flow of energy from the interior. As a result, parts of the surface become cooler and somewhat less bright than the rest.

Flares

From time to time a brilliant display called a flare is observed in the vicinity of sunspots. A flare appears suddenly as an irregular trail of light extending over thousands of miles of surface. It brightens for a few minutes, then slowly fades away.

Flares seem to be outbursts of energy dammed up under sunspots. They appear most clearly on pictures taken in hydrogen light. This shows that flares are eruptions of hot hydrogen.

Sunspots and flares come in 11-year cycles. For several years there are more and more spots, and each group is larger than the one before. Flares also increase in number and size. Then activity slows down, as the Sun begins a "quiet" period of several years.

Scientists kept this cycle in mind when planning the International Geophysical Year of 1957-58. They chose a time when sunspot activity reached a peak. Then they were able to carry on a world-wide patrol of the Sun during one of its stormy periods. Observations were made on the ground and also by means of instruments carried in balloons, rockets, and satellites. These studies were continued into the quiet period of 1964-65, called the International Years of the Quiet Sun—IQSY.

The Energy of Stars

Scientists have learned from the spectrum of sunlight that hydrogen is the most abundant element on the Sun. Next in abundance comes the gas helium. From studies of other stars, it is known that their make-up is like the Sun's. All have great supplies of hydrogen and helium.

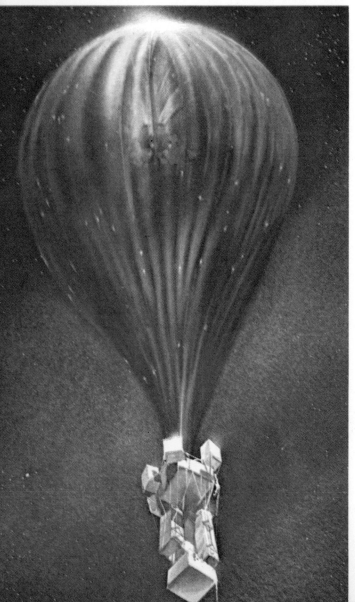

Balloon-borne telescope for photographing the Sun

42

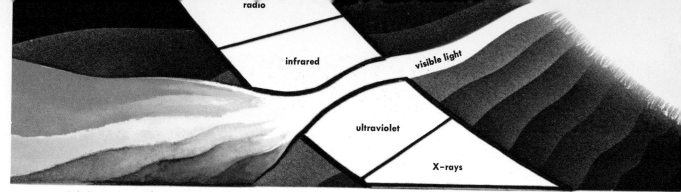

Light rays and invisible energy waves from the Sun make up the electromagnetic spectrum

In the stormy interior of a star, pressures are enormous, and temperatures are in the millions of degrees. These conditions set off atomic reactions. Hydrogen atoms crash into other atoms. After a series of swift transformations, the hydrogen atoms fuse—combine—to form helium. Each helium atom is made of the matter that was in four hydrogen atoms. But a small particle of that matter is missing. It has been converted into energy. This energy keeps the Sun hot, and keeps the atomic reactions going on and on.

Every second, about 700 million tons of hydrogen turns into helium. In a year, 22 million million tons of hydrogen is used up. Yet this is just a small part of the Sun's mass of hydrogen, which amounts to about 1,494,000,000,-000,000,000,000,000,000 (1 octillion, 494 septillion) tons. With such a supply, our star will go on shining for billions of years.

Radiation

Energy from the Sun travels in waves of different length, radiating in all directions. Some of these wave lengths form visible light. There are also ultraviolet rays, which are shorter, and X rays, which are still shorter. Heat waves (in-frared) are longer, and radio waves are still longer. This whole range of radiation is called the electromagnetic spectrum.

Most of the Sun's radiation is lost in space. Just a small portion hits a few targets—the planets and their moons. The amount striking the Earth is only one two-billionth of the Sun's output. Yet even this comes to five million horsepower per square mile of surface.

Many wave lengths are stopped and absorbed in the atmosphere. This is fortunate, since the X-ray and ultraviolet radiation would be harmful to us and other living things. But the visible wave lengths get through, bringing light and warmth and making the Earth a world where life can exist.

Orbiting Solar Observatory

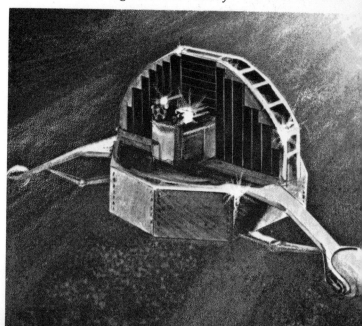

Temperatures on Mercury's sunny side are high enough to melt lead

THE INNER PLANETS

When Mercury and Venus appear in the evening, they are always near the setting Sun. When they rise before dawn, then, too, they are near the Sun. This is because they circle in inner orbits, closer to the Sun than ours. As we watch them for several months, they seem to shift back and forth from one side of the Sun to the other. Mercury's path is shorter, since its orbit is smaller. And it is always low over the horizon, close to the hidden Sun.

Through a telescope, we see that both Mercury and Venus have phases like the Moon's. When either planet comes between us and the Sun it is invisible, since the dark side faces us. As it moves on, a little of the lighted side shows as a crescent. Farther along, half of the lighted side shows. As the planet moves around behind the Sun, we see the whole lighted side, which looks like a small full Moon.

Mercury

Mercury is about the size of the Moon, but harder to examine because of its distance. An object on the Moon may be visible through a telescope if it measures a mile across. An object on Mercury would have to be 50 or 100 times as large to be seen at all. Even then it would appear only as a little spot without details. Such things as plains and mountain ranges would make hazy shapes of slightly different brightness or color. Such shapes are all we can see on Mercury's surface.

Nevertheless, astronomers have found out a number of interesting things about Mercury. It reflects as much sunlight as the Moon would reflect at the same distance from the Sun. Evidently its surface is like the Moon's.

Mercury compared to the Atlantic Ocean

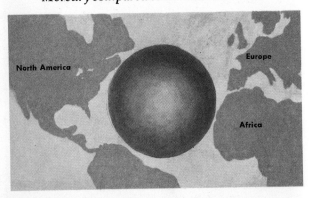

44

Mercury has no atmosphere. Scientists are not surprised at this. Mercury's gravity is too weak to hold gases. Because there is no air, the sky above Mercury is not blue. Even in broad daylight the sky is black, with the Sun and stars shining together.

Mercury turns around on its axis just as the Earth does. But it rotates much more slowly than our planet. As a result, the day on Mercury is almost 59 times longer than ours.

The sunlit side becomes hot enough to melt lead. It heats up to 750 degrees Fahrenheit while on the dark side temperatures may drop to about 450 degrees below zero. Under such conditions, life cannot exist.

Venus

Beautiful Venus outshines the stars. This is partly because it is near us, but also because much of its sunlight is reflected by clouds.

The clouds mean that Venus has an atmosphere. This was discovered in 1761 by Michael Lomonosov, a Russian scientist. Lomonosov kept watch over Venus just before the planet was to pass across the face of the Sun. As the little black disk approached the Sun, Lomonosov noticed a faintly glowing ring around it. This, he concluded, was Venus' atmosphere lighted by sunlight.

We are not surprised to find that Venus has an atmosphere. The planet is nearly the Earth's twin in size and mass. Since its gravity is nearly as strong as the Earth's, it can hold gases. Indeed, Venus has more atmosphere than the Earth. This is shown by the fact that the

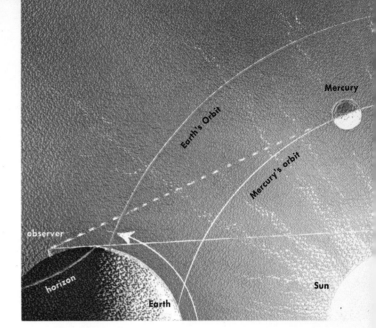

Why Mercury is seen near the setting Sun

tops of the clouds float 60 miles high—much higher than clouds above the Earth.

Just the barest hint of water has been detected in the spectrum of Venus, so the clouds are probably not made only of water droplets and ice crystals. What sort of particles are they made of? This is one of the mysteries that scientists would like to solve.

Lomonosov discovered the atmosphere of Venus

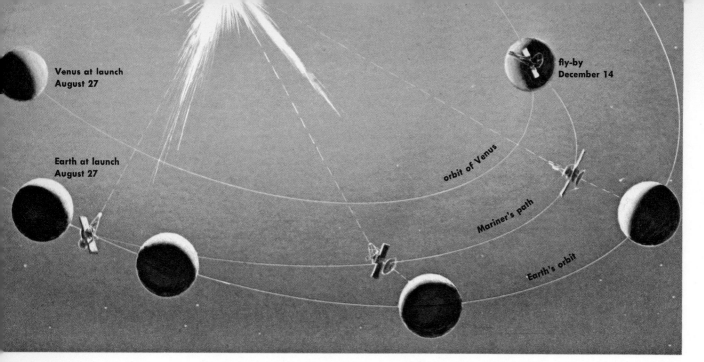

Venus at launch
August 27

Earth at launch
August 27

orbit of Venus

fly-by
December 14

Mariner's path

Earth's orbit

The fly-by of the spacecraft Mariner 2 past the planet Venus

Temperatures on Venus

Since Venus is nearer the Sun than we are, it receives more light. This could make the planet warmer than the Earth. But the clouds reflect a large portion of the light, and this could make Venus cooler.

Scientists have taken Venus' temperature by measuring heat radiated from the upper atmosphere. This method gives temperatures around 40 degrees below zero, but the figures tell nothing about conditions deeper down, near the surface.

A great deal of carbon dioxide has been found in Venus' atmosphere—much more than we have on Earth. This and the clouds make a "heat trap." Light comes down through the atmosphere and is absorbed—changed into heat waves. Carbon dioxide and the clouds prevent the heat waves from escaping, so they warm up the atmosphere. The earth's lower atmosphere is warmed in a similar way.

In recent years a new method has been used to take Venus' temperature. It measures short radio waves produced by heat. The waves are weak, but they go through the atmosphere of Venus and reach the Earth.

Each of the inner planets has phases like the Moon's

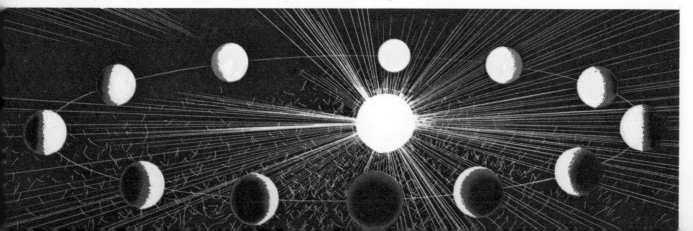

The radio waves come from Venus' atmosphere, not the surface. They indicate that at certain levels temperatures are higher than the melting point of lead.

It is equally hot on the dark side of the planet. This shows that winds in the thick, dense atmosphere carry the heat everywhere. Is it also that hot at Venus' surface? If so, living things could not exist there.

Probe by Spacecraft

In 1962 the American spacecraft Mariner 2 flew past Venus. It was launched by a rocket which first lifted it 115 miles high. There the rocket and spacecraft turned into a "parking" orbit and coasted a short distance around the Earth. The rocket fired again, increasing the speed to more than 25,000 miles an hour. Mariner 2 then broke away from the Earth's gravity and went into an orbit around the Sun.

At the start of its solar trip, Mariner 2 was moving at the Earth's speed—66,000 miles an hour. If it had kept going at this speed it would have stayed in the same orbit as the Earth, and would never have approached Venus. The problem was to slow it down so it would fall part way toward the Sun and cross the orbit of Venus.

To accomplish this, the escape was timed so that Mariner 2 was headed backward, in the opposite direction from the Earth's motion. Its backward motion slowed it down. It fell toward the orbit of Venus and finally crossed it just after Venus had passed. Because Mariner 2 had fallen closer to the Sun

than Venus, the spacecraft speeded up and overtook the planet. This happened 109 days after launching, just at the time when Venus and the Earth were only 26 million miles apart.

Mariner 2 passed within 22,000 miles of the planet. Its instruments to measure heat and radio waves were working, and their information was broadcast.

On the Earth, great dish antennas had been trained on Mariner 2 at stations in California, Australia, and South Africa. As the Earth turned, one station after another tracked the spacecraft and received its signals.

From some of these signals it would seem that Venus' surface temperature is about 800 degrees Fahrenheit on both the lighted and the dark side.

In 1967 a Soviet craft, Venus 4, dropped a capsule with instruments deep into the atmosphere of Venus. The temperature there was found to be 536 degrees Fahrenheit. This makes it seem unlikely that life could exist on Venus.

The clouds rise 60 miles high around Venus, and because they conceal the surface it is impossible to observe rotation. But radar signals bounced from the surface indicate that the planet makes a full turn in a time equal to about 244 of our days. Since its year—the time of its trip around the Sun—is 225 days, a day on Venus is longer than a year!

Venus about to pass across the Sun's disk

PLANET NUMBER 3

The third planet from the Sun was the hardest to "discover." For thousands of years men did not suspect that the Earth was a planet. They did not even dream that it was round.

Philosophers of ancient Greece began to wonder about the Earth's true shape. When traveling south to Egypt, they saw strange stars over the southern horizon. From this they realized that the Earth's surface is curved, and that northern and southern places are under different parts of the sky.

The Earth's Shape and Size

The philosophers watched eclipses of the Moon and saw that the edge of the Earth's shadow is always round. They realized that only one shape—a sphere—will cast a rounded shadow from any position. Once they had guessed the Earth's shape, the philosophers tried to figure out its size. This problem was

Eratosthenes measured the Earth with a shadow

solved by a man named Eratosthenes. He lived in the city of Alexandria, in northern Egypt. Eratosthenes thought of a way to measure the Earth when he heard a report from southern Egypt. In the city of Syene, at noon on the first day of summer, a post cast no shadow. This showed that the Sun was directly overhead. In Alexandria at the same time, a post did cast a shadow. The Sun was not directly overhead. It was at a small angle from the vertical.

Eratosthenes found this angle to be 7.2 degrees from the vertical. Now, there are 360 degrees in a circle. And 7.2 is exactly one-fiftieth of 360. Therefore, he reasoned, the distance between Syene and Alexandria was one-fiftieth of the distance around the Earth. Since the two cities were 500 miles apart, the distance around the Earth was 50 times 500, or 25,000 miles.

How Eratosthenes calculated the size of the Earth

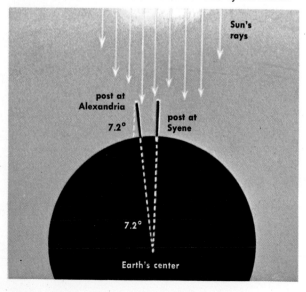

The Earth's Motions

In ancient times, nearly everybody thought the Earth stood still in the middle of the Universe. The starry sky turned around it once a day; the Sun went around it once a year.

An astronomer named Aristarchus had another idea. He said: "These motions may not be real. If the Earth turned, the sky would seem to turn. If the Earth went around the Sun, the Sun would seem to go around the Earth."

No one could prove whether this idea was right or wrong. After a while it was forgotten, and people continued believing in a motionless Earth encircled by the moving Sun and planets.

Astronomers were mainly interested in predicting the positions of the planets. At times an outer planet seems to be slipping backward in its orbit. We know now what causes this. The Earth is passing the planet in the race around

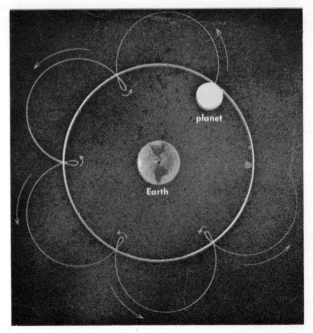

Planetary motion as pictured by Ptolemy

the Sun. The astronomer Ptolemy proposed another explanation: the planet loops along in a small circle as it travels around the Earth. Its motion in the small circle makes it seem to go forward, then backward, then forward again.

Ptolemy worked out a complicated system of such motions. Astronomers used his system for centuries to predict the positions of the planets.

Around the year 1500, astronomers began to find that Ptolemy's system did not fit their observations. The young Polish astronomer Copernicus read of the forgotten idea that the Earth might be moving, and decided to test it with his own observations. All the rest of his life he searched for the truth about the motions of the heavenly bodies. Just before he died, Copernicus published his work in a great book. In his system, the Sun stands in the center of its kingdom, and the planets circle it in their proper order. After Mercury and Venus comes planet number three, our own Earth.

The solar system according to Copernicus

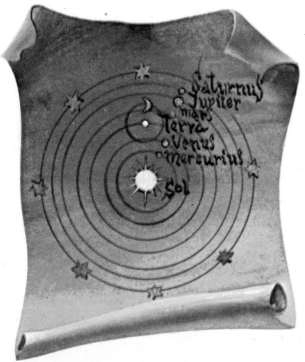

49

How a spacecraft can avoid the Earth's radiation rings

MAGNET WORLD

Why does a compass needle point north and south? William Gilbert, an English scientist, worked on this problem three centuries ago. Gilbert knew that the compass needle is a magnet. Like every other magnet, it has a north pole and a south pole. If a compass is brought near

William Gilbert

a bar magnet, each pole is attracted by the opposite pole of the magnet.

"The whole Earth must be a magnet," Gilbert said. "It must have magnetic poles somewhere in the north and south which attract the poles of the compass needle."

A search was begun for the Earth's magnetic poles, and in time they were discovered. They lie in the Arctic and Antarctic, about 1,000 miles from the geographic poles.

Later, scientists found that the Earth's magnetism extends far above its surface. "Lines of force" go up from each magnetic pole, curve around the planet, and loop back to the opposite magnetic pole. They form a magnetized region called the magnetosphere.

Rings of Radiation

In the far North and South, the night sky often glows with flickering streamers of light. This display is the aurora, or northern and southern lights. Many years ago astronomers noticed that the aurora was brightest when there were many sunspots and flares. They suspected it was caused by charged particles from the Sun shooting along the lines of force into the Earth's atmosphere.

This idea could not be checked until there was some means of sending instruments into the space around the Earth. When the first artificial satellites were launched, they were equipped with detectors to count charged particles. When particles hit a detector, radio signals would report the hits to stations on the ground.

James Van Allen and a team of American scientists studied records of hits. They noted where they were most numerous, and in this way located the regions of main activity. It was found that most particles are in two great rings around the Earth. The inner boundary of the nearer ring is a few hundred miles up. The outer part of the farther ring fades into space thousands of miles away.

The rings are shaped by the Earth's magnetic field. Particles from the Sun curve in along the lines of force. They are trapped and shoot back and forth from one magnetic pole to the other. Occasionally some of them shower into the atmosphere around the magnetic poles. They collide with gas particles, making them emit radiation, and this causes the glowing light of the aurora.

If an astronaut were to go through the ring region, it would seem like ordinary empty space. All the particles in the whole magnetosphere do not add up to more than the weight of a man.

Yet the particles are dangerous. Shooting from pole to pole in a few seconds, they would go right through the human body, and a large dose of them would cause serious damage, and even death.

Astronauts circling the Earth travel beneath the dangerous rings. When the Apollo 8 astronauts flew through them on their way to the Moon in 1968, their vehicle was protected by a lead shield. At times of solar flare activity, it may be safer to shoot a vehicle through the opening in the rings over one of the magnetic poles.

The compass works because the Earth is a magnet

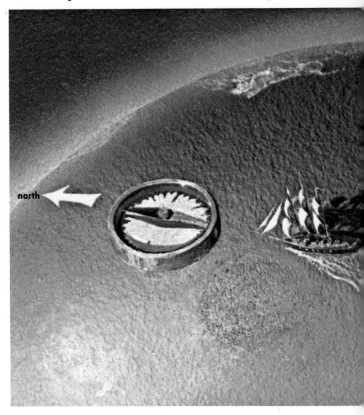

51

Various markings appear as Mars rotates

IS THERE LIFE ON MARS?

There is good reason to ask this question about our neighbor planet in orbit number four.

Mars is a bit more than half the size of the Earth. Its gravity is only two-fifths as strong as the Earth's, but the pull is enough to hold a thin atmosphere. The density of this atmosphere at the surface is that of air 15 miles above the Earth. Nitrogen is probably the main gas. There is carbon dioxide but little if any oxygen. There is some water.

Mars travels about 141 million miles from the Sun. This is near enough for the planet to receive a fair amount of light and heat. At the equator, noontime temperatures go as high as 85 degrees Fahrenheit.

The period of rotation is 24 hours and 37 minutes. This gives Mars a day and night like ours, so each side of the planet is warmed and cooled in turn. The atmosphere holds a certain amount of heat. As a result, night temperatures around the equator drop "only" to 60 degrees below zero. It might be worse.

The axis of Mars is tilted about as much as the Earth's. Because of this, Mars has seasons. When it is winter in the northern hemisphere, a white ice cap spreads around the North Pole. During the northern summer, this ice cap shrinks and nearly disappears. Meanwhile, an ice cap spreads around the South Pole.

Since the ice appears and disappears quickly, it must be very thin. Perhaps it is only a coating of hoarfrost an inch or so thick. There is not enough water on Mars to form great layers of ice like those found on the Earth in Antarctica and Greenland.

Much of the surface of Mars is a rusty color, which probably comes from sand and rock containing iron. Around the zones of the ice caps there are greenish-gray stretches. As the ice cap shrinks, these areas become darker, possibly from water soaking into the ground. Meanwhile, the greenish-gray areas expand toward the tropics. In the autumn, these same areas turn rusty.

Project Gulliver

For a long time, astronomers have wondered if the greenish-gray areas on Mars are covered by plants of some kind. After all, the climate of those areas is no worse than that of the Earth's Antarctic, where tough little lichen plants grow on the bare rock.

Scientists tried to find out if certain kinds of bacteria could live under conditions like those of Mars. They kept the bacteria in "Mars jars" in the laboratory, and the bacteria lived, grew, and multiplied.

There are several different plans to search for signs of life on Mars. One is called Project Gulliver after the device that will be sent to the planet. The whole thing is about the size of a man's two fists. It contains a little chamber holding broth in which bacteria can grow.

When Gulliver lands, three little bullets will fire from it, carrying sticky strings. The strings will then be reeled in by little motors. Dragging along the ground, they will pick up particles of soil and possibly some bacteria, and will bring them back into the chamber of broth.

The broth contains materials which are radioactive. If bacteria are present, they will grow and multiply, and radioactive gases will be released in the chamber. This will cause a radiation counter to click, and the clicks will be radioed to receiving stations on Earth. If the signals come, they will say: "There is life on Mars."

Device for detecting possible microscopic life on Mars

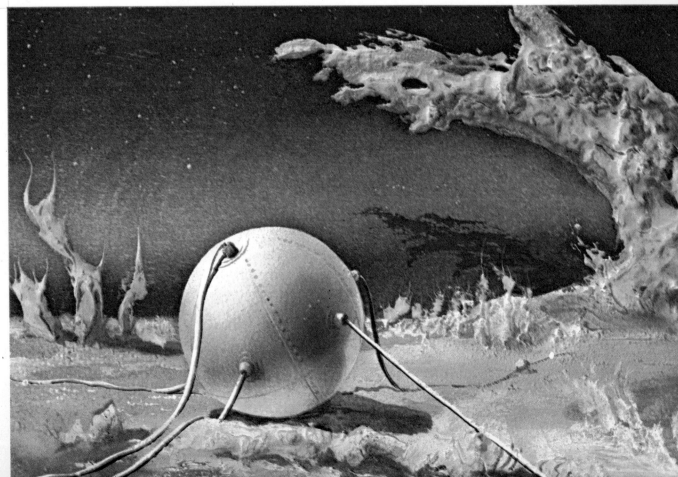

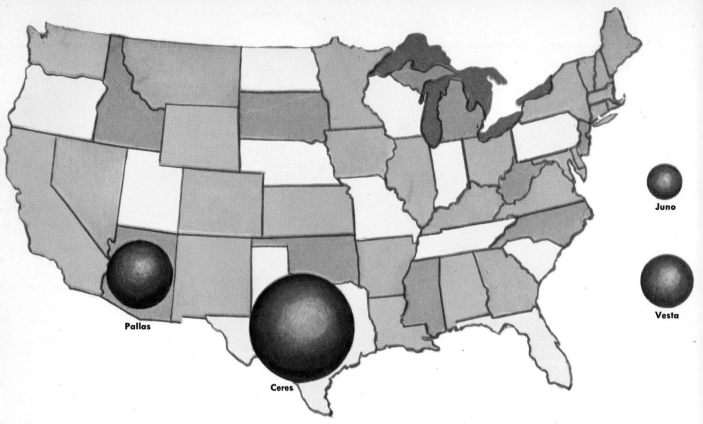

Some of the larger asteroids compared to the United States for size

THE ASTEROIDS

A gap of space nearly 350 million miles wide stretches between the orbits of Mars and Jupiter. At one time astronomers thought there might be a planet traveling somewhere in this gap.

In 1801 a point of light was discovered moving in an orbit between Mars and Jupiter. Night after night astronomers followed it. Thinking the body was a planet, they named it Ceres after the Roman goddess of the harvest.

When Ceres was measured, it turned out to be only 450 miles in diameter. Alas! This was no planet. Soon, three other little bodies like Ceres were discovered. Later, when astronomers began to photograph the sky, they found hundreds of such bodies. A dozen turned out to be over 100 miles in diameter; some were less than a mile.

All these bodies are barren chunks of rock. Through a telescope they look like stars, so they are called asteroids, which means starlike.

Asteroids are located by examining photographs taken with exposures of an hour or more. During an exposure, motors turn the telescope in the opposite direction from the Earth's rotation. This keeps it aimed at the same place in the sky. As a result, the stars photograph as points of light. But the asteroids, because they move against the background of stars, photograph as streaks.

An asteroid's trail on a time exposure

So many asteroids have been found that astronomers have run out of legendary names for them. So they have been given names such as Edna, Fanny, and Agnes. Some have been named after places—among them Ohio, California, and China.

Asteroids have different shapes. Some are spheres, but many more seem to be irregular chunks like mountains flying through space. This suggests they may be pieces broken from some larger body. Possibly the asteroids are fragments of a shattered planet. Or they may be material that never came together to form a planet.

All the asteroids travel around the Sun in the same direction as the planets. Each moves in its own orbit. About 2,000 orbits have been figured out. Most lie between Mars and Jupiter. But some orbits are very elongated, and go beyond the gap. One asteroid curves in closer to the Sun than Mercury. Another swings out nearly to the orbit of Saturn.

The orbits of a few asteroids cross above or beneath the Earth's orbit. The asteroid Apollo came within three mil-

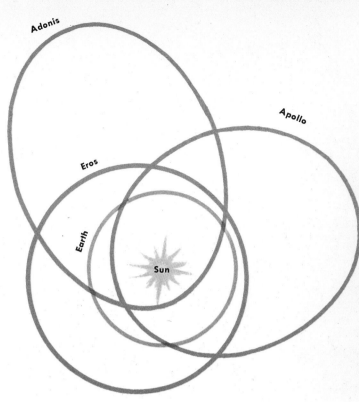

Orbits of the Earth and three asteroids

lion miles of our orbit in 1932. Adonis came within one million miles in 1936, and Hermes came within half a million miles in 1937.

Is there danger that the Earth will collide with an asteroid? Such collisions probably happened in the past, clearing the space around our orbit. Now collisions are less likely to happen.

Most asteroids revolve in a belt between Mars and Jupiter

Halley's Comet, which last appeared in 1910, is expected to return in 1986

COMETS

In former times, people were terrified when a comet trailed across the sky. They thought it was a sign of the end of the world.

A comet first appears as a spot of bright haze. It rises and sets like the stars, but moves slowly along a course of its own. Night after night it comes closer and grows larger and brighter.

Gradually, a filmy tail stretches out from the haze. The tail may become millions of miles long and extend across the whole sky. It is made of stuff so thin that stars can be seen through it. Meanwhile, a starlike nucleus appears in the middle of the comet's "head." It is probably a cluster of small objects held together by their gravitational pull.

After the invention of the telescope, astronomers observed a number of comets carefully. They were found to be the size of a large planet, or larger. They travel in very long orbits. A comet becomes visible when it loops close around the Sun. Then it swings away and gradually disappears.

If the orbit is open, the comet goes off into space, never to be seen again. But if the orbit is closed, the comet can be expected to return.

In 1682 the English astronomer Edmund Halley made observations of a bright comet which appeared that year. He calculated its orbit, and compared it with comets which had been observed in 1531 and 1607. All three, he decided, were the same comet, which returned approximately every 76 years. Halley predicted that it would be seen again about 76 years later. It arrived when expected, late in 1758, and was named Halley's Comet in his honor.

The Tail Tells

The tails of comets always point away from the Sun. Astronomers have found that they glow partly with reflected sunlight. This shows the presence of dust particles which reflect light.

Halley's Comet   *Morehouse's Comet*

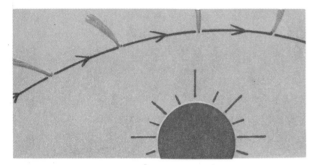

A comet's tail always points away from the Sun

Most of the light, however, is produced in the tail itself. When molecules of gas in the tail are hit by ultraviolet rays from the Sun, they begin to glow.

While a comet is traveling in cold regions far from the Sun, its gases are frozen around the dust particles. When it approaches the Sun, the gases evap-

orate. A portion of the gas and dust streams out, forming a tail. Astronomers think this material is driven off by the solar wind—a "wind" of atoms thrown from the Sun.

Where do comets come from? One theory starts from the fact that the whole solar system is moving through space. In passing through thin clouds of matter, the Sun sweeps up gas and dust particles. Such material follows the Sun in a trailing veil. It falls toward the Sun, but sometimes a batch is pulled aside by the attraction of an outer planet. The batch misses the Sun, curves around it, and becomes a comet.

Certain comets cross the Earth's orbit. What would happen if one of them should collide with the Earth? No comet has ever been known to make a direct hit. In 1910, however, the tail of Halley's Comet brushed the Earth. The only result, so far as could be seen, was a faint glow in the sky, caused by gas and dust particles of the tail. The Comet is expected to return again in 1986. What will happen then?

The parts of a comet   *The Great Comet of 1861*

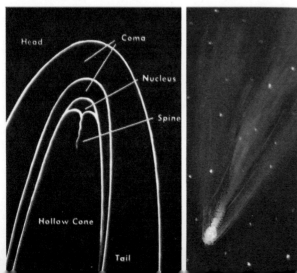

METEORS AND METEORITES

On a clear, moonless night, you may see ten meteors an hour. These "shooting stars" are caused by bits of matter—meteorites—which turn into glowing vapor as they plunge into the atmosphere. They appear as streaks because of their speed, which is about 25 miles a second. The streak begins around 70 miles high and ends at about 40 miles.

At certain times, meteors fall in "showers." There are many more than usual, and they come from the same part of the sky. One shower meets the Earth around the tenth of August. It is called the Perseids because it comes from the direction of the constellation Perseus.

Astronomers have found that the showers are caused by swarms of meteorites traveling in regular orbits. The orbits are close to those of certain comets. In 1846 a comet with a period of 6½ years split in two. In 1852 the twins returned, but never appeared again. But in 1872, on the day when the Earth crossed the orbit of the vanished comet, there was a tremendous downpour of meteors. Apparently, meteorite swarms are the remains of comets.

Besides the meteorites which make visible streaks, thousands of smaller ones bombard the Earth every second of the night and day. They turn into a fine dust which drifts through the air, to settle unnoticed on land and sea. Several thousand tons of this material is added to the Earth every 24 hours.

Occasionally, a portion of a large meteorite gets through the atmosphere

Friction with the air heats up a meteorite
Crater in Arizona blasted by a giant meteorite

58

The 34-ton Ahnighito meteorite found by Admiral Peary in Greenland

and reaches the Earth's surface. Many such meteorites have been found and analyzed. Some are iron mixed with nickel. The majority are stone, but a number of the stony meteorites contain much iron and nickel—more than is found in ordinary rocks of the Earth.

Most known meteorites are small—the size of a marble, an egg, or a fist. A few weigh several tons. Meteorites as large as this are rare. When one streaks in, heat and pressure usually cause it to explode in the air.

Once in a great while a large meteor appears in the form of a "fireball." One fell over Siberia in 1908. Bursts of light trailed along its path, probably caused by drops and gobs of melted metal. The remainder blew up with a roar that could be heard far away. Trees were knocked down over a wide area.

The Earth has several scars made by large meteorite hits in the past. One is the famous Meteor Crater in Arizona. It is a gaping hole nearly a mile across and 600 feet deep. Scientists dug in the

area looking for a giant meteorite. They found only small pieces of iron and one chunk weighing half a ton.

What happened to the rest of the meteorite? Its impact heated the ground and the meteorite itself. Much material vaporized, causing an explosion which shattered the meteorite.

Scientists believe that iron meteorites come from the interior of a large body. Perhaps they are fragments of a planet that broke up long ago.

The Earth meets a meteor swarm in a comet's orbit

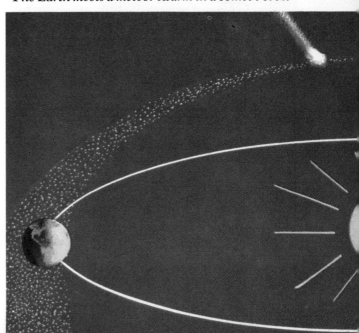

59

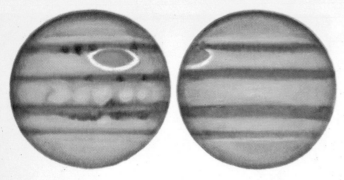

The Great Red Spot shifts as Jupiter rotates

JUPITER

Jupiter, giant of the planets, circles 480 million miles from the Sun. Though far away, it is bright. Its broad surface is covered with clouds which reflect a lot of sunlight, so the giant is easily seen as it passes from one constellation to the next on its 12-year trip around the Sun.

Galileo discovered the moons of Jupiter

Jupiter is 88,000 miles in diameter—large enough to hold 1,300 Earths. Yet its mass (amount of matter) is only 318 times greater than the Earth's. Astronomers have learned this by observing the paths of Jupiter's moons.

These figures show that Jupiter is made largely of light material—gases. They form layers thousands of miles thick around a solid core, which is probably rock and metal.

Two gases have been identified—ammonia and methane. Hydrogen also is thought to be present. An atmosphere made of these gases would be poisonous to living things.

Since Jupiter is far from the Sun, ammonia and other gases may be frozen into thick shells around the planet. It is possible, however, that the clouds hold enough of the Sun's heat to keep some of the ammonia liquid. There may be an ocean of it.

Jupiter's clouds probably consist of ammonia crystals floating in hydrogen. A strange marking, the Great Red Spot, extends over 2,000 million square miles of the clouds. The Red Spot turns around the planet regularly, showing that Jupiter rotates in 9 hours and 50 minutes.

Because of this rapid spinning, the clouds stream around the planet in wind belts parallel to Jupiter's equator. The edges of the belts are irregular and always changing. This shows that tremendous storms rage in Jupiter's atmosphere.

The rate of spinning at the equator is 27,000 miles an hour. It has made the planet bulge around the middle, leaving the polar regions flattened.

Jupiter's Moons

Jupiter has 12 known moons. Four are large and bright enough to be seen through a small telescope. They circle around Jupiter's equator.

As we see them, the moons are arranged in line. Because of their circling, they continually shift along the line. One after another crosses behind or in front of the planet and moves to the other side.

Two of these satellites are larger than Mercury; the other two are about the size of our Moon. The nearest circles Jupiter in less than two days; the farthest, in about 17. Like our Moon, all keep the same face toward their planet.

The eight other satellites are smaller. One circles close to Jupiter. The rest travel farther out, in elongated orbits. Four seem to be misfits. Though all the other moons circle in the direction of Jupiter's spinning, these four go the "wrong" way. Why is this? Are they asteroids that Jupiter pulled into its system?

The four large moons were discovered by Galileo in 1610. At that time people still thought that all heavenly bodies circled around the Earth. Even most scholars believed this. They could not accept the theory of Copernicus which said that the Earth moves around the Sun. The teaching of this theory was considered wrong, reckless, and against religion.

Imagine Galileo's excitement as he looked through his telescope and watched the four satellites circling around Jupiter. He wanted to share his discovery with the whole world. He in-

Jupiter as it may appear from one of its moons

vited scholars to look through his instrument, and they saw the moons.

"Here," said Galileo, "are bodies that do not go around the Earth. They go around Jupiter. Is it really so strange, then, that the Earth should revolve around the Sun?"

The doubters were not convinced. Galileo wrote of his discovery and defended the ideas of Copernicus. He was arrested and jailed for this, but his jailers could not destroy the evidence in the sky.

In time, astronomers found the eight smaller satellites of Jupiter. They have been numbered in the order of their discovery. Satellites I to IV are known as the Galilean Moons in honor of the man who first saw them.

Saturn and its moon Titan compared to the Earth for size

SATURN

Saturn, the planet with the rings, travels in an orbit 400 million miles beyond the orbit of Jupiter. Its trip around the Sun takes 29½ of our years. Its day is 10 hours and 14 minutes long, and rapid rotation has given the planet a bulging and flattened shape.

Saturn is large enough to hold 700 Earths, but its material is more than seven times lighter than the Earth's. This means it has only a small core of rock, surrounded by thousands of miles of ice and gases.

The gases are the same as Jupiter's. Because of temperatures far below zero, most of the ammonia must be frozen into an icy shell. Above this lies a thick atmosphere of hydrogen and methane, carrying clouds of ammonia ice. The planet's spinning causes the gases and clouds to stream around it in great wind belts.

The curious, beautiful rings encircle Saturn above its equator. The innermost ring begins 7,000 miles up. It is so thin that the body of the planet shows through it. The next ring is wider and brighter. Then comes a gap of space, beyond which lies the outermost ring. The whole series is 40,000 miles wide but only a few miles thick.

Saturn's axis is tilted, and this means

From Saturn, the rings might look like this

Saturn as seen in different years

the rings also are tilted. As the planet moves along its orbit from year to year, the rings appear in changing positions. At one time their northern or upper surface is seen; years later, the lower surface. Between these positions, the rings are edgewise to the Sun and to us. Then they cannot be seen at all, and Saturn seems ringless.

Each ring revolves, but not as a solid band. The inner part moves faster than the outer. This shows that the rings are made of separate particles. Each particle moves in its own orbit, at its own speed. The particles are probably lumps of ice and rock.

Beyond the rings is a system of circling moons. Ten have been discovered so far. One of them, Titan, is nearly as large as Mars. Its reddish color suggests a rocky surface. Traces of methane have been detected around it, showing that Titan has a thin atmosphere. Some of the other moons are unusually bright, possibly because of a coating of ice.

The outermost moon, only 150 miles wide, travels in an orbit over eight million miles from the planet. It is a misfit like the outer satellites of Jupiter. Instead of going in the direction of Saturn's rotation, it goes the other way around. Perhaps it is a "captive" from the asteroid belt.

A small moon or asteroid probably supplied the material of Saturn's rings. As it came closer and closer to the planet, there were tremendous pulls upon it due to gravitation and its own rushing speed. The satellite was ripped apart. It shattered into millions of bits of ice and rock, which spread around the planet, forming its rings.

Astronomers predicted the position of Neptune before it was discovered

URANUS, NEPTUNE, PLUTO

Until 1781 no one dreamed there might be a planet beyond Saturn. Then William Herschel in England, while mapping stars in the constellation Gemini, noticed a faint greenish body that shifted slightly from night to night. It turned out to be the seventh planet, Uranus. With its five known moons, Uranus orbits 900 million miles beyond Saturn. It takes 84 Earth years to complete a revolution.

Like Jupiter and Saturn, Uranus is a "gas-giant" flattened by rapid rotation. In one way, it is unlike any other planet. Its axis is tilted so far that Uranus "lies on its side." In fact, the North Pole is slightly south of the orbital plane. If this pole is considered the South Pole, then Uranus rotates backward!

Number 8—Neptune

After the discovery of Uranus, astronomers observed the planet carefully. Something was very strange. Uranus wandered from the path it should follow according to the law of gravitation. An unknown body seemed to be pulling it away from the Sun. Was there an eighth planet beyond Uranus?

In 1846 two men, Leverrier in France and Adams in England, were trying to figure out the orbit of the unseen planet. Each determined that it was then in the constellation Aquarius.

Leverrier wrote to an astronomer at the Berlin Observatory and gave him the calculated position of the planet. The

The green giants, Uranus and Neptune

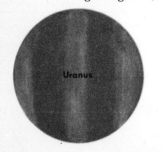

Uranus

Neptune

astronomer trained his telescope in that direction, and there the planet was!

Neptune, the eighth planet, is another frozen gas-giant. It has two known moons. Planet and moons circle nearly 2,800 million miles from the Sun, and take about 165 of our years to make one revolution. Neptune will not be back in the position where it was discovered until the year 2011.

Number 9—Pluto

After the discovery of Neptune, astronomers realized that the wanderings of Uranus still were not completely accounted for. They became convinced that a ninth planet, somewhere beyond Neptune, was tugging on Uranus.

Just where was the mysterious planet? Astronomers calculated its position, and searched the sky for years. In 1894 Percival Lowell built an observatory at Flagstaff, Arizona, for the purpose of studying Mars. He also looked for the unknown planet, predicting that it would be found in Gemini.

Thousands of photographs were taken and compared. Using an instrument called the blink microscope, astronomers examined negatives of a region made at different times, to see if any object had changed position.

In 1930 a young astronomer at Flagstaff, Clyde Tombaugh, found an unmapped moving object on negatives of Gemini. It turned out to be the missing planet, which astronomers had failed to discover earlier because it was much fainter than expected. The planet was named Pluto after the god of the underworld.

Pluto was discovered from photographs

The name fits, for Pluto travels in a dark region about 3,700 million miles from the Sun. Its year is 248 Earth years long. Coming after the giants, Pluto seems a dwarf, for it is hardly larger than Mercury. Its orbit is unusually elongated. At its narrowest part, it crosses Neptune's orbit. This may mean that Pluto was once a moon of Neptune which escaped and became a planet.

Comparing photographs with a blink microscope

Whirlpools of gas and dust revolved around the newborn Sun

CREATION OF THE SUN AND PLANETS

Think how orderly the solar system is. All the planets travel around the Sun in the same direction. Their orbits lie nearly in one plane. The Sun and all the planets except Uranus spin from west to east.

What started the Sun and planets moving in this regular way? How did the solar system begin?

Astronomers have been trying for a long time to solve the mystery of creation. Two hundred years ago the philosopher Immanuel Kant proposed an idea, which was developed by the mathematician Pierre Simon de Laplace. In the beginning, according to their theory, a huge cloud of gas and dust was slowly rotating in space. Gravitation pulled most of the cloud's matter into the center, where it formed a great sphere. Compression heated the sphere until it became a star, the Sun.

As the Sun-cloud shrank, it spun faster and faster. The edge around the equator spun so fast that it whirled away from the rest and became a rotating ring. Other rings were thrown off in the same way, one after another. As time went on, the matter in each ring collected into a planet, which continued circling in the old orbit of the ring.

Notice how well this theory accounts for the shape and motions of the solar system. The planets naturally move in one plane, and circle the Sun in the same direction.

Later on, astronomers realized that the theory did not agree with a certain important fact. The Sun rotates slowly. If it were the remainder of a rotating cloud which threw off matter for the planets, the Sun should be spinning at least 50 times faster.

From Dust to Worlds

Most astronomers now agree on a somewhat different picture of creation. A great cloud of hydrogen and dust was drifting in space. Under the pull of its own gravity, the matter of the cloud was drawn toward the center. Streaming inward, it formed a gigantic whirlpool, just as flowing water may form a whirlpool. The whirling made the cloud flatten out into a shape like a wheel.

A great mass of matter gathered in the center. As it was pressed together it heated up. The hydrogen reaction began, and the mass became a star.

In the rest of the wheeling cloud, smaller whirlpools formed. Some were the beginnings of planets. Others were the beginnings of moons.

In each planet whirlpool, dust gathered into lumps. The lumps were held together by droplets of liquid, and were frozen together by crystals of ice. Gradually, the lumps collected into larger bodies. The largest of all the bodies gathered in the rest and grew into a planet. The planet continued the spinning motion of the whirlpool.

While the whirlpools were becoming planets, different amounts of their gases escaped. They were pushed away into

The Kant-Laplace theory of planet formation

space by the pressure of sunlight. Little Mercury lost all of its gases; the next three planets lost most of theirs.

But Jupiter and the other giants were large and far from the Sun. At their distances, the pressure of sunlight was too weak to drive off all gases. Great quantities of gases remained, and the giant planets, with their powerful gravity, held them forever after.

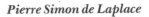

Pierre Simon de Laplace

Stars like the Sun are strewn through the farthest reaches of space

PART THREE

The Starry Universe

THE BILLIONS OF STARS

On a clear, moonless night, the sky is crowded with twinkling stars. About three thousand can be seen with the unaided eye. Millions are visible through a large telescope.

As one astronomer said, "There are probably more stars in the sky than there are grains of sand on all the seashores of the world."

Astronomers divide the sky into 88 regions, each marked by a constellation. Many of the constellations have the names of legendary heroes and of sacred animals—for example, Orion the Hunter and Taurus the Bull—which were given to them by sky-watchers of ancient times.

Stars are Suns

The stars appear as points of light only because they are very far away. Actually, they are gigantic suns.

By analyzing starlight, astronomers have learned that the stars are made up of elements like the Sun's. Hydrogen is the most abundant, and helium comes next. The stars shine because atomic reactions are working in them, producing energy that streams through space in the form of light.

You have probably noticed that stars are not all of the same color. Many are white, but some are yellow and some blue-white. A few are red. Our own Sun is a yellow star. The different colors are due to different temperatures. The blue-white stars are the hottest. The red stars are the coolest.

How Far Away?

If a star is fairly near, its distance can be measured in the way a surveyor measures the distance of a mountain. He sights the mountain from two separate points, then measures the distance between the points. This gives him a base line, which forms one side of a triangle. The other two sides are the sight lines to the mountain. The surveyor measures the angles at the two ends of the base line. From these angles and the length of the base line, he calculates the length of the sight lines. This is the distance to the mountain.

The greater the distance to be measured, the longer the base line must be. To measure the distance of a star, the astronomer uses the longest possible base line—the diameter of Earth's orbit around the Sun—186 million miles. The astronomer sights the star against the background of more distant stars. Six months later, when Earth is on the opposite side of its orbit, he sights the star again. The sight lines and the diameter of Earth's orbit form a triangle. By measuring its angles, the astronomer finds the distance of the star.

Even the nearer stars are so far away that it is inconvenient to give their distance in miles. A much larger unit is used—the light year. This is the distance light travels in a year. In a second, it goes 186,000 miles. In a year, it goes almost six trillion miles.

The nearest star is over four light years away. This is Proxima of Cen-

taurus, which can be seen only from the southern hemisphere. Another near star is Sirius, 8½ light years away.

Only 55 known stars are within 16 light years of the Earth. Light that you see from all the others started out before you were born. The light from many started out before your grandparents were born. Some stars are so far away that they are photographed by light which left them before there were people on the Earth. Perhaps some of these stars have ceased to shine, and only their light remains.

Brightness · Size · Temperature

Astronomers classify stars according to their brightness—or, as they say, magnitude. A certain degree of brightness is first magnitude. A brightness 2½ times less is second magnitude. A brightness 2½ times less than that is third magnitude. And so on.

A first-magnitude star may appear bright simply because it is near. Another star may be faint because it is very far away. To find out a star's real brightness, astronomers allow for its distance.

The size of a star is calculated from its surface temperature and the amount of heat it radiates. The temperature is shown by the star's color. The heat radiation is shown by its brightness. Knowing both, the astronomer figures out how much surface the star must have to give off that amount of heat.

Stars of Many Kinds

Sometimes, when a star is examined through a telescope, it turns out to be

Measuring the distance of a nearby star

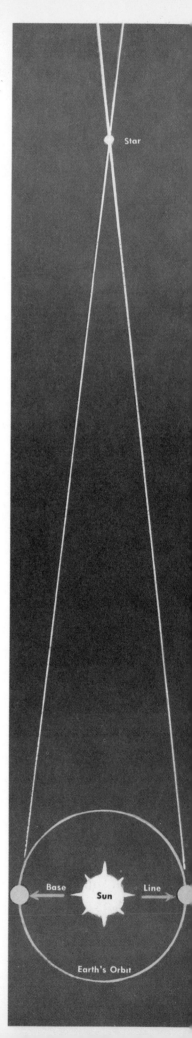

two stars. They may simply be located one behind the other, but so far apart that they have no real connection. In other cases, two stars are a real pair, linked by gravity and revolving around a common center. If the two-star system is placed edgewise to us, each star in turn passes in front of the other and eclipses it for a while. The double star turns dim, but brightens up when the eclipse is over and the light of both members of the pair is seen again.

There are also triple stars, quadruplets, and even sextuplets. In these systems, the members are connected like dancers swinging one another around.

Any star that changes in brightness is called variable. In addition to the eclipsing pairs, there are variable stars that have real changes in brightness. They flare up, turn dim, and flare up again. Some stars go through these changes in a few hours. Others take days, months, or years. Astronomers think such stars pulsate—expand and contract, over and over again. Polaris, the North Star, pulsates in this way, brightening and fading in a period of four days.

Now and then a star blazes up and becomes many thousand times brighter than before. After a few days or months it grows dim again. Then it is found to be surrounded by an expanding cloud of matter, which it has blasted off into space. Such a star is called a nova.

About twice in a thousand years, a supernova flares up somewhere in our part of the Universe. This is a star which suddenly becomes millions of times brighter, then fades away and disappears. A supernova was observed by the Danish astronomer Tycho Brahe in 1572. Today no star is visible where it appeared, but radio signals have been received from there, showing that some sort of activity is going on.

In 1054, Chinese astronomers observed a supernova in the constellation Taurus. Now, no star is found in that location. Instead, there is a great bright cloud, which is expanding rapidly. Because it is shaped somewhat like a crab, it has been named the Crab Nebula. Nebula means cloud. Evidently, a supernova is a star that explodes and destroys itself.

Unseen Companions

Every now and then astronomers find a star that wobbles slightly, as if pulled by some unseen body circling it. When the mass of such a body is calculated, it turns out to be great enough for a planet larger than Jupiter.

At the distance of other stars, planets would be much too small and dim to be photographed. Yet astronomers believe they exist. It would be strange if the Sun alone, among thousands of millions of stars, gave birth to a family of planets.

Very likely, millions of stars have planets. Some may be worlds like the Earth, surrounded by air and receiving enough light and warmth to give them mild climates. Many such Earth-like planets may be homes of life. Perhaps intelligent beings dwell on some of them —beings who look into the sky and ask questions like ours. Have they noticed the star we call the Sun? Have they wondered if it has planets, and possibly one where life exists?

STARS THROUGH THE YEAR

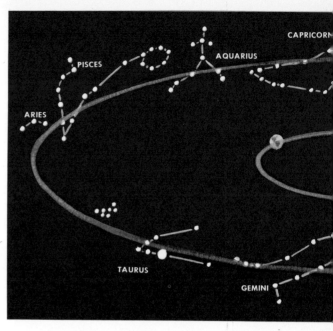

Twelve constellations form the zodiac

On an automobile trip, we can tell where we are from landmarks. On our trip around the Sun, we know where we are from skymarks.

Different constellations are seen from different parts of our orbit. To understand this, remember that the Earth and Sun are surrounded on all sides by constellations. In winter we are on one side of our orbit, and look out at night toward the constellations on that side. As the Earth turns and morning comes, we face the constellations on the other side of our orbit. They are there but we cannot see them, for they are hidden by the Sun's glare.

During our yearly journey, the constellations appear to shift toward the west. That is because the Earth is moving the opposite way. Pick out a constellation and see.

A handsome constellation to watch is Orion. It rises early on November evenings, and sets in the west before dawn. Each evening, Orion is a little farther toward the west, so it rises and sets earlier. By February, it is high in the sky at nightfall. By May, it is already setting in the west at nightfall. By the beginning of summer, we have gone around to the opposite side of our orbit. We face Orion when we face the Sun, which blots out the light of the stars.

Orion, early evening

Two weeks later

Four weeks later

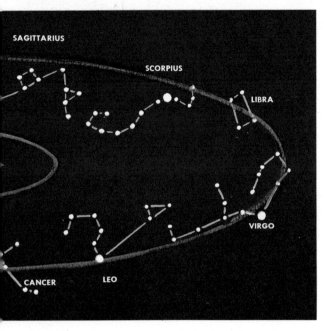

The zodiac seems to encircle the solar system

Formerly, people believed that the stars influenced their lives. Astrologers made a business of explaining this supposed influence. They claimed they could tell a person's fortune according to what sign of the zodiac he had been born under. Today a few people still go to astrologers to have their fortunes told. This is nonsense. We study the stars, not to learn about ourselves, but to understand the Universe around us.

The zodiac constellation figures

The Zodiac

Because of the Earth's motion along its orbit, the Sun seems to move. It rises and sets in one constellation, then in another. From the middle of April to the middle of May, it rises and sets in Taurus the Bull, which is near Orion. Gradually, it shifts eastward to the next constellation, Gemini the Twins.

In a year, the Sun appears to move through 12 constellations: the Bull, the Twins, the Crab, the Lion, the Virgin, the Scales, the Scorpion, the Archer, the Goat, the Water Carrier, the Fishes, and the Ram. After a year, it is back in the Bull again.

In ancient times the Sun's path through the constellations was named the zodiac—the circle of animals. The circle was divided into 12 equal parts. Each part was marked by a constellation, and each had a special sign that was used on charts and instruments.

The Big Dipper can be seen all year long from most of the northern hemisphere

STARS AROUND THE POLES

You can easily become acquainted with the constellations around the North Pole of the sky. The most striking among them is called the Great Bear, Ursa Major. Several of its stars form the Big Dipper.

Look carefully at the star at the bend of the handle. This is Mizar, which has a fainter companion, Alcor. Both stars were named long ago by Arab astronomers. In their time, finding Alcor was considered a sign of good eyesight. Today Alcor is rather easy to see. Perhaps it has become brighter.

When you look at Mizar through a telescope, you discover that it is not a single star, but a pair of them. The two seem like one to the naked eye because they are so close.

The Pole Star or North Star, as you remember, is located by sighting along the two stars opposite the handle of the Dipper. The Pole Star itself belongs to another constellation, the Little Dipper.

It is the last star in the handle. The astronomical name of the Little Dipper is Ursa Minor, the Little Bear.

A legend tells how the bears got into the sky. Hera, the wife of the god Zeus, was jealous of the beautiful nymph Callisto and had her changed into a bear. One day Callisto's son met the bear in the woods. Not knowing she was his mother, he lifted his knife to attack her. But before he could do so, Zeus turned the boy into a little bear and placed him and his mother in the sky.

A constellation named Draco, the Dragon, winds between the bears, then swings in a curve beyond the Little Bear.

On the opposite side of the Pole Star from the Big Bear is the constellation Cassiopeia, named after a legendary queen. Its stars form the letter W or M, depending on the way you look at them.

Nearby is a constellation named after Cepheus, the husband of Cassiopeia.

The main stars of Cepheus form the outline of a house with a peaked roof. The star at the corner farthest from the Pole Star is Delta of Cepheus. It is a pulsating star that reaches its greatest brightness every 129 hours. The brightening and fading that we see now occurred nearly two centuries before Columbus discovered America, for Delta of Cepheus is about 650 light years away.

As the Earth turns, the constellations near the Pole Star seem to wheel around it. In an hour, each goes one twenty-fourth of the way around. If you could observe them night after night with instruments, you would find that the constellations are always a little farther along in their turn than they were the night before. In a year their advance adds up to one complete turn around the Pole Star. This extra turn is due to the Earth's journey around the Sun.

Stars of the Far South

If you travel southward, your view of the sky changes. From the Equator, you see the Pole Star right at the northern horizon. The constellations around it now rise and set.

When explorers from Europe sailed into southern seas a few centuries ago, they found no guiding star at the Pole. But a certain group of stars, the Southern Cross, was useful to them because its longer arm points south.

Constellations of the far south have no legendary Greek and Roman names, since they were unknown to the people of ancient Greece and the Near East. They were named in recent times by mariners and explorers. Some were

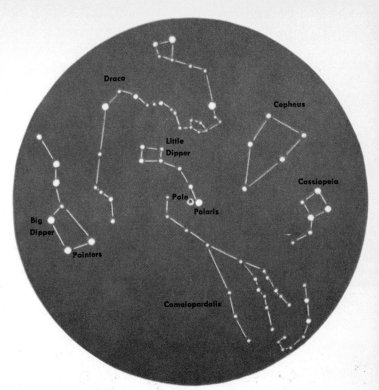

Constellations around the North Pole of the sky

given animal names, among them the Peacock and the Toucan, but others were named after instruments—for example, the Clock, the Compass, the Telescope, and the Microscope.

Today, the stars are still signposts in the sky. They are signposts for travelers in space as well as travelers on Earth.

Constellations around the South Pole of the sky

75

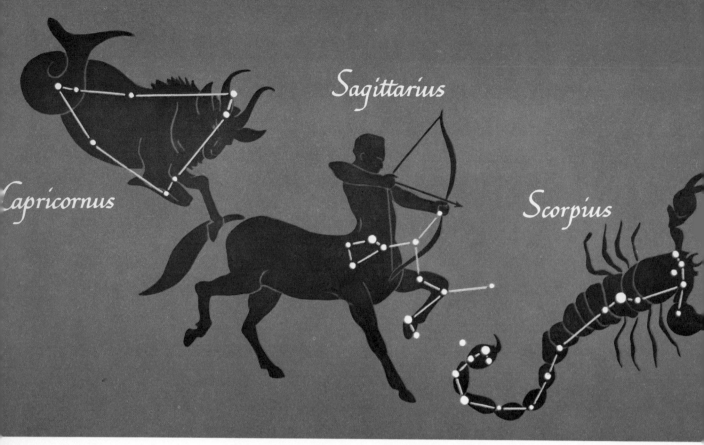

The zodiac constellations seen in spring and summer

CONSTELLATIONS

At the top of these two pages and the next two are the zodiac constellations. Follow them from right to left. This is the order in which they rise.

At the bottom of the opposite page and page 79 are several constellations that do not lie in the zodiac. Inside the covers of this book you will find charts showing nearly all the constellations visible from the northern hemisphere.

In spring, the constellation Leo, the Lion, rises above the eastern horizon early in the evening. You will find it by sighting from the two stars of the Big Dipper's bowl near the handle. They point toward Leo's brightest star, Regulus, which is said to be the heart of the Lion. Regulus is a blue-white star 84 light years away.

Look nearer the horizon to find the next zodiac constellation—Virgo, the Virgin. Its stars are faint, except Spica, a blue-white star 120 light years away.

Perhaps the most beautiful star of spring is Arcturus. To find it, look out along the curve of the Big Dipper's handle until you come to an orange star. This is Arcturus. It is in the constellation Boötes. In one legend Boötes is a hunter chasing the bears. In another he is a shepherd who invented the plow. The Big Dipper is his plow.

Boötes faces a small, dim half-circle of stars—Corona, the Crown. East of it is a large constellation named after Hercules, the hero of many adventures.

As summer comes, new constellations appear. Among them is beautiful Cygnus, the Swan, also known as the Northern Cross. Deneb, its brightest star, is 465 light years away.

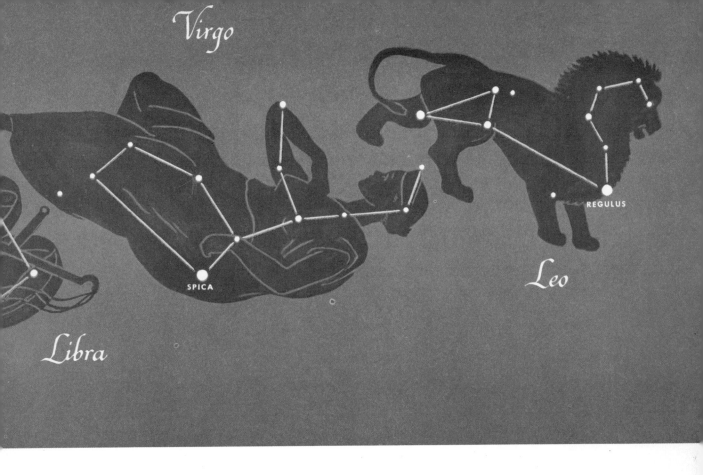

Virgo

SPICA

Libra

REGULUS

Leo

South of the Cross is the small constellation Delphinus, the Dolphin. East of the Cross is Lyra, the Lyre. Its main star, Vega, 26 light years away, is the brightest summer star.

South of the Lyre is Aquila, the Eagle. Its brightest star, Altair, is 16 light years away. Altair forms a great triangle with Deneb and Vega.

Scorpius, in the zodiac, is named after the scorpion that killed Orion. Near the center of the constellation is a brilliant red star, Antares, called the Rival of Mars. Actually, Antares is so enormous that it would hold several million bodies the size of Mars.

Next along the zodiac is Sagittarius, the Archer. Stars in the center form a figure like an upside-down dipper, sometimes called the Milk Dipper.

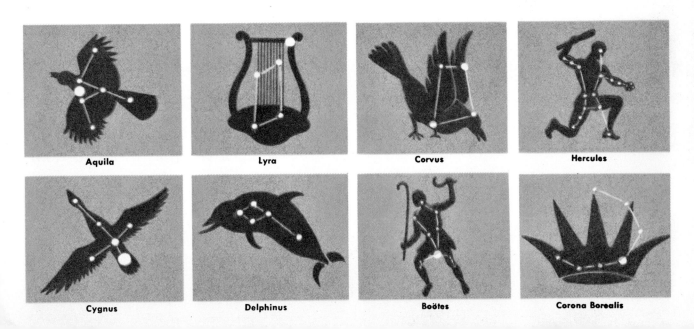

Aquila

Lyra

Corvus

Hercules

Cygnus

Delphinus

Boötes

Corona Borealis

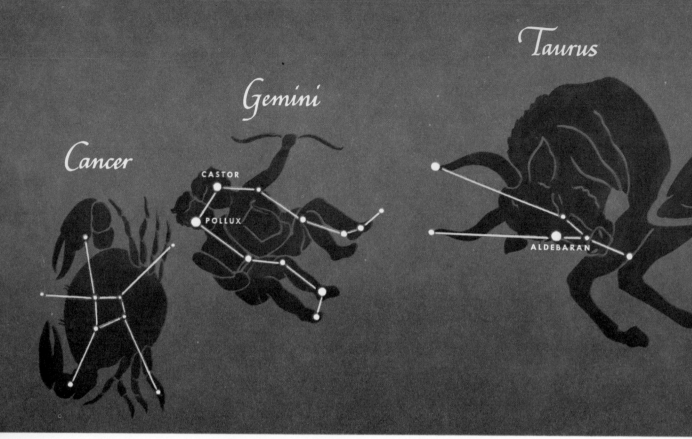

The zodiac constellations seen in autumn and winter

In autumn, we see the striking constellation Pegasus, named after the legendary winged horse of the Greeks. You will recognize it as a great square not far from Cassiopeia. Nearby is the constellation Perseus. Perseus was a hero who rescued and married Andromeda, the daughter of Cassiopeia. According to the legend, Cassiopeia boasted that her daughter was more beautiful than the sea nymphs. This displeased the god of the sea, who had Andromeda chained to a rock as a sacrifice to a monster. Just as the monster was about to devour her, along came Perseus on the winged horse. He was carrying the head of a hideous creature he had just killed— the snaky-haired Medusa. At the sight of the head, the monster turned to stone, and Andromeda was saved.

Perseus is supposed to be holding the head of Medusa. One of the creature's

eyes is a variable star that brightens and fades every 69 hours. Its Arabic name, Algol, means the demon. It is really a pair of stars which revolve around a common point and eclipse one another.

During autumn and winter, we look out toward the bright zodiac constellations Taurus and Gemini. But the real lord of the sky is Orion, marching along south of them. Three bright stars form Orion's belt, from which hangs a dagger made of three fainter stars. In one hand Orion holds a club. In the other he holds a lionskin as a shield.

Orion was a mighty hunter, rival of the gods. To punish him, the gods sent a scorpion which bit his foot and killed him. The Scorpion is on the opposite side of the sky, so it is seen in summer.

The red star at Orion's shoulder is Betelgeuse, a super-giant. Its diameter is four times the distance between the

Aries

Pisces

Aquarius

Earth and Sun. Betelgeuse is 300 light years from us, yet appears bright because it radiates 3,600 times more light than the Sun.

Rigel, the blue-white star near Orion's knee, is 540 light years away. Its diameter is one-tenth that of Betelgeuse, yet it appears a little brighter. Its real brightness is ten times greater. Rigel is one of the brightest stars known.

Sirius, in the Big Dog constellation, is the brightest of all the stars we see—mainly because it is much nearer than most. It is white-hot, with a surface temperature of 40,000 degrees Fahrenheit.

Sirius is a double star. Its companion, nicknamed the "pup," is a dwarf only twice as wide as the Earth. But its matter is so compressed that a spoonful would weigh a ton on Earth.

Cassiopeia   Auriga   Pegasus   Orion

Perseus   Canis Minor   Andromeda   Canis Major

CLUSTERS AND NEBULAS

The stars are separated by unimaginable reaches of space. Suppose they were the size of baseballs, and the spaces between them were reduced to the same scale. Then the average distance between one star and its neighbor would be over 4,000 miles.

In most regions the stars are more than ten light years apart. In others they are closer, forming groups known as open clusters. These clusters are not just accidental patterns like the constellations. They are real groups of stars moving together and affecting one another's motions.

Inside the square of the Crab is a well-known open cluster, the Beehive, made up of stars about four light years apart. Other open clusters are the Pleiades and the Hyades, which can be seen with the unaided eye. Their location is shown on the chart inside the back cover.

More than 300 open clusters are known. Each contains from 20 to 1,000 stars. Their average diameter is 20 light years.

Another type of group is the globular cluster, in which the stars are about one light year apart. One such cluster can be seen in the constellation Hercules. It is marked M13 on the charts inside the front cover of this book. To the unaided eye it looks like a blurry star. No wonder, for it is 34,000 light years away.

The cluster M13 photographs as a bright ball of stars. Even the largest telescope cannot separate most of them. M13 is thought to contain about 100,000 stars. Its diameter is estimated at 100 light years. About 100 other globular clusters are known. All are very far away.

Most star clusters have no names. They are identified by numbers given to them in astronomical catalogues. M13, for example, is a number from the Messier Catalogue.

Nebulas

Charles Messier was a French astronomer of the 18th century who spent years searching the sky for comets. In the

A dark nebula, the Horsehead in Orion

The globular cluster M 13 in Hercules

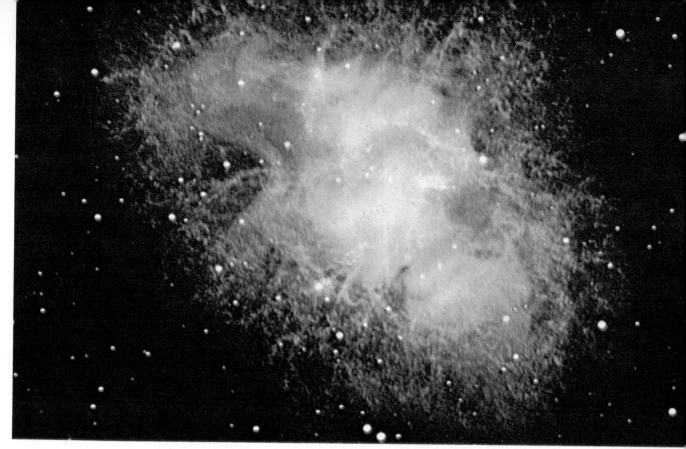

The Crab Nebula is probably the remains of an exploded star

course of his search he found 103 hazy patches that resembled comets but clearly were something else, since they did not change position among the stars. He called them nebulas—clouds—and listed their location in order to avoid confusing them with comets.

Later, Messier's nebulas were found to be various kinds of objects. Some are star clusters. Others are really clouds of gas and dust, set aglow by starlight. Such a nebula can be seen around the middle star of Orion's dagger. Through a telescope it looks like a great swirl of mist. The nebula is 1,500 light years away and 30 light years across.

Some nebulas appear as dark patches outlined against bright areas in the background. A famous dark nebula is the Horsehead in Orion, visible only through a telescope.

Dark or bright, the clouds of matter will not remain forever as they are. In many clouds, the matter will gradually pull together and form stars. And in some cases, no doubt, leftover matter will form systems of planets.

The Ring Nebula M 57 in Lyra

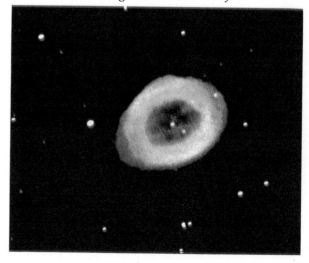

THE MILKY WAY

Look overhead on a moonless summer night, and you see the most magnificent sight in the heavens—a filmy trail of light streaming north and south across the whole sky. This is the Milky Way. Its Greek name, the Galaxy, means milky.

The trail begins in the constellation Perseus, goes through Cassiopeia, Cepheus, and Cygnus, continues down through Sagittarius and disappears beyond the southern horizon. If you travel south of the Equator, you will see the rest of the Milky Way trailing across the entire southern sky.

Look at the Milky Way through a telescope, and you see that it is made up of hosts of stars crowded close together. The whole, long trail is a vast assemblage of thousands of millions of stars.

Shape of the Galaxy

In the 1780's William Herschel and his sister Caroline studied the Milky Way with telescopes they had built. They saw that some of the stars are bright, but many are faint, as if lying beyond the bright ones. Farther still, swarms of even dimmer stars fade into space.

Herschel realized that the stars of the Milky Way are arranged in a flat system which is turned edgewise toward us. We see stars beyond stars because we are looking deep into the system.

What would we see if we could look at the flat side of the Galaxy? Is it a disk, an oval, a square, or some irregular shape?

Herschel thought of a way to find out. He assumed that where the stars are thickest, the Galaxy is widest; where they are thinner, it is narrower. Taking sample areas in various parts of the Milky Way, Herschel and his sister counted stars by the hundreds and thousands. In one case, they found 588 stars in an area about a quarter of the size of the full Moon. After years of sampling and counting, Herschel decided that the system was an irregular disk.

The Milky Way includes all the stars we see in the sky. Among them is the Sun with its circling planets, located about half way out from the center of the Galaxy. From the Earth we have very different views in different directions. When we turn away from the Milky Way we see few stars, since we are facing outward and look through only a small part of the width of the system. When we face the Milky Way, we see millions of stars, since we are looking deep into the Galaxy.

Before 1918 it was thought that the globular clusters might belong to the Galaxy, but their location was uncertain since their distance had not been determined. To find out whether or not they were really in the Galaxy, astronomers needed a scale for measuring the distance of very far-away systems.

In 1913 the American astronomer Henrietta Leavitt discovered such a scale. While studying variable stars that pulsate, she found that the period of their brightening and fading is related to their real brightness. The longer the period, the brighter the star. Once the real brightness is known, it can be compared with the apparent brightness, and the difference tells the distance of the star.

Harlow Shapley, of the Harvard College Observatory, saw that the new scale could be used for locating the globular clusters. He observed variable stars in the clusters, determined their distance, and in this way found that the clusters are really in the Galaxy. They are grouped around a region in the constellation Sagittarius. This region, bright with crowded millions of stars, forms a central nucleus of the Galaxy.

Photo of a portion of the Milky Way

WHIRLPOOLS OF STARS

Astronomers made an important and exciting discovery when they trained the giant telescopes and cameras on some of the objects listed as nebulas.

Even in Herschel's time, scientists had thought that the nebulas might be something more than clouds of gas and dust. They said: "Perhaps the nebulas look like clouds only because they are very far away. If we could see them better, they might turn out to be star systems. Possibly they are island universes like our Galaxy, scattered through the farthest reaches of space."

The Great Nebula

The nebula M31, in the constellation Andromeda, is barely visible to the naked eye as a little blur of light. When it was first photographed through small telescopes, the nebula turned out to be a spiral structure tilted in our direction.

Photo of the Great Nebula in Andromeda

At its center is a brilliant nucleus, around which long streamers unwind.

Later, pictures taken through the 100-inch reflector on Mount Wilson revealed that the spiral is an immense whirlpool of stars.

Astronomers have found that the Great Nebula, as M31 is commonly called, is made up of familiar kinds of stars. Among them are variable stars that pulsate. By observing the variable stars and determining their distance, astronomers have learned that the Great Nebula lies two million light years away. It is far outside our Milky Way Galaxy. It is, in fact, another galaxy—a separate "island universe."

Many other galaxies have been photographed and studied. A number are spheres, ovals, disks, and irregular shapes, but most are spirals with unwinding arms. Some of the spirals are broadside to us; some are edgewise; others are tilted at various angles.

Structure of Our Galaxy

What type of galaxy is the Milky Way? Since we are inside the system we cannot see its shape, but certain facts hint at what it is.

The Milky Way has a number of features in common with the Great Nebula and other spirals. They contain a fair percentage of hot blue stars, as our system does. They also have vast clouds of hydrogen and dust, as our system does. Other types of galaxies seem to lack both of these features.

When such facts were discovered, astronomers concluded that the Milky Way was probably a spiral. Proof of this finally came through the use of radio astronomy.

It was found that hydrogen sends out radio waves of a certain length. This made it possible to discover where the hydrogen is distributed in our Galaxy. In the Great Nebula and other spirals, it is concentrated along the arms.

Astronomers trained radio telescopes on the Milky Way, recorded the signals of hydrogen, and traced the regions where it is most plentiful. The shapes of these regions formed an outline of arms. This proved that our Galaxy is like the Great Nebula—a spiral.

On photos of an edgewise spiral, a dark band is commonly seen running along the equator of the system. This band seems like a strip of empty space dividing the galaxy into halves. Actually, it is caused by clouds of gas and dust along the spiral arms. The clouds conceal the stars behind them.

When you follow the Milky Way through the constellation Cygnus and southward, it seems to be split by a gap of starless space. This dark gap is really an effect caused by gas and dust clouds which hide the stars. If our Galaxy could be photographed edgewise from far away, it would look like others, with a dark band running along its equator.

On the same photograph, the nucleus of the Galaxy would form a bright bulge. It is made up of more than 100 globular clusters, each containing from several thousand to a million stars. The rest of the stars are strung along the arms. Altogether, the Galaxy has nearly 100 bil-

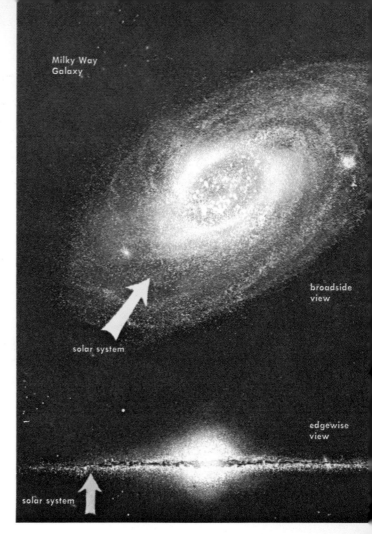

Our Galaxy as it might appear from far away

lion stars. The diameter of the whole vast system is more than 100,000 light years.

Astronomers have found that the Galaxy turns as a great whirlpool, with gas and dust and stars all swirling around the center. Speed depends on the distance from the center. Near it, the motion is faster; farther out, slower. The Sun's region of the whirlpool moves about 160 miles a second, or more than 500,000 miles an hour. The speed is great, yet the system is so vast that it takes more than 200 million years for the Sun to make a full circuit. The whole history of man has happened during a small fraction of one turn.

Photographs show that galaxies vary in structure

SCALE OF THE UNIVERSE

The spiral galaxy nearest to ours, the Great Nebula in Andromeda, has many stars like the Sun. We suppose that a number of these stars have planets, including some like the Earth.

If intelligent beings exist somewhere in the Great Nebula, could we communicate with them by radio? Remember that radio waves travel at the speed of light. Since the Great Nebula is two million light years away, it would take that long for a message to reach it.

Suppose we broadcast a message today. And suppose inhabitants on a planet of the Great Nebula received our message two million years from now and sent an answer. It would take another two million years for the answer to arrive here.

Galaxy of Galaxies

Our Galaxy has two companions—smaller, irregular star systems, which can be seen from the southern hemisphere. They are called the Magellanic Clouds, and they seem like stray pieces of the Milky Way. They move around the Galaxy as moons circle a planet.

Schmidt telescopic camera

86

The Great Nebula also has two smaller companions, both spirals. These systems, together with our Galaxy and the Magellanic Clouds, belong to a group of about a dozen galaxies. Astronomers call it the Local Group.

The Local Group is surrounded by a vast gulf of space. Beyond it lie other groups and clusters of groups. The great telescopes have photographed more than a million of the brighter galaxies within a distance of 500 million light years around us.

The 200-inch reflector on Mount Palomar can "see" a billion light years into space. Galaxies do not thin out at this distance, so there are probably millions still farther away. Astronomers expect, when the range of telescopes is increased, to find that galaxies are just as thick in the space beyond.

There seems to be a limit, however, beyond which we shall never be able to see. The spectrum patterns of light from the galaxies show that they are moving away from us. Actually, they are all spreading out from one another. The whole Universe appears to be expanding. The most distant known galaxies are evidently moving away at a rate of 60,000 miles a second. This is one-third the speed of light. Much farther away, there may be galaxies receding at the speed of light. If so, we shall never see them, for their light does not travel fast enough to reach us.

In imagination, we have gone into the farthest reaches of space. If we lived "out there" in some other galaxy, think how impossible it would be to discover the solar system. First we should have to find the Local Group, then the Milky Way Galaxy. Among its millions of stars, we should have to make out, in one of the spiral arms, the ordinary star known as the Sun. Even with a 200-inch telescope, we would not be able to discover that the Sun is lord of a little family of circling bodies, and that one of them is the home of intelligent beings who are trying to understand the scale of the Universe.

The Clouds of Magellan were named after the explorer

A rocketeer's idea for a future space station to be assembled while in orbit

PART FOUR

Exploring Other Worlds

AN ENGINE FOR
SPACE FLIGHT

Before this century, only dreamers and storytellers thought of travel to other worlds. In 1865, when Jules Verne wrote a story about a voyage to the Moon, most people did not take it seriously.

In the story, a space ship carrying three passengers is fired from a giant cannon. It escapes from the Earth and circles the Moon. Would this be possible? The ship would have to reach a speed of seven miles a second in the instant after firing. This would be a fantastic gain of speed, or acceleration. But say it was done, and the ship was not destroyed at once. Such acceleration would be too much for the travelers. They and their instruments would be squashed as flat as pancakes. Then the space ship would heat up and vaporize from friction with the air.

Two young persons began to think seriously about these matters. One was a Russian, Constantine Tsiolkovsky, who later became a school teacher. The other was an American, Robert Goddard, who became a university professor. Both wondered about the possibility of flight into space. Then they began to calculate. They were dreamers, but scientific dreamers. They worked for years on the problem of space flight. Finally, without even knowing about one another, both solved the problem in the same way. Now, because of their work, the dream of travel to other worlds is about to come true.

The Rocket

Tsiolkovsky knew that no ordinary engine could be used in a space ship. Automobile and airplane engines use oxygen from the air to burn their fuel, but there is no oxygen in space.

Tsiolkovsky began to consider the rocket as an engine. In his time it was used mainly in fireworks. The skyrocket is a tube containing a charge of gunpowder. The powder burns rapidly at the lower end. Hot gases shoot down, and the rocket shoots up.

The rocket works according to the law of motion which says: "To every action there is an equal and opposite reaction." For example, when you dive from a raft, your action of springing forward kicks the raft the other way.

As gases rush down from the explosion chamber, the rocket shoots up

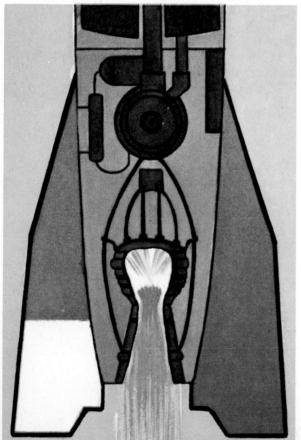

In the rocket, fuel burns in a chamber near the tail. Hot gases from its combustion expand rapidly. Since the back of the chamber is open, the gases escape there without pushing against the rocket. But they do push against the forward end of the chamber, and this shoves the rocket forward. The faster the gases expand and escape, the greater the speed of the rocket.

Tsiolkovsky calculated that a rocket would need a lot of fuel to reach a speed of several miles a second. Liquid fuels like alcohol and gasoline have more energy than gunpowder. Therefore, he decided, the rocket should burn liquid fuel.

Oxygen is needed for burning. Since there is none in space, the rocket would have to carry its own supply. Liquid oxygen would be in one tank and fuel in another. Pumps would spray them into the rocket's combustion chamber.

To reach the speed of escape, Tsiolkovsky's rocket was designed in several stages. Stage one would fire until its fuel was used up, then drop away. Then stage two would fire, burn its fuel, and drop away. And so on. Each stage would start at the speed of the one before, and add to it. Each would be lighter, so it could accelerate with less fuel. The last stage would reach a speed of seven miles a second. Then, with its fuel burned out, the rocket would coast silently into space.

Tsiolkovsky also designed a space station to go into orbit around the Earth. Later, various other types of space stations were projected. One was to be in the shape of a great wheel that would spin around. Men inside it would feel a force like gravity and be able to work and move around as though they were on the Earth.

Tsiolkovsky designed his rockets when Russia was still ruled by tsars. The government would not spend money to have them built. Finally, under the Soviet government, the rockets were built, and one of them launched the Earth's first artificial satellite.

Robert Goddard, like Tsiolkovsky, found that the engine for space should be a stage rocket burning liquid fuel. He obtained money and other help for his work and was able to go from calculation to experiment.

Goddard built the world's first liquid fuel rockets, and launched them on test flights. Though small, they were "ancestors" of the great rockets which now launch men into orbit around the Earth and send instruments to neighboring worlds.

Robert Goddard launched the first liquid-fuel rocket in 1926. Constantine Tsiolkovsky (below) *was the first scientific investigator of space flight*

LAUNCHING A SATELLITE

It is night at a rocket base. Under the glare of floodlights, a gleaming metal giant stands on its launching pad, aimed at the sky. It is as tall as a ten-story building, and weighs as much as a freight car. At dawn the rocket will take off. In its nose is a package of instruments. If all goes well, this package will become a satellite of the Earth.

Countdown

A steel gantry stands beside the rocket. On its platforms, men are busy giving each part a final check. This is the countdown. A certain amount of time is allotted for checking each part. Time signals come from the control tower. Each signal begins with T, for take-off. "T minus 60" means 60 minutes of countdown to go. If repairs are needed at any point, mechanics flash a red light, and the countdown stops. When they flash green, it starts again.

During the last hour, the rocket's tanks are filled with fuel and oxygen. The mechanics and engineers leave the pad. The countdown goes on. "T minus three seconds, T minus two, T minus one." The last count, "T Zero," is drowned out by a thunderous roar, and the great rocket rises on a pillar of fire.

Stage one develops a tremendous thrust. This is needed to get the giant rocket started and to boost it through

The powerful engine of stage one must boost the rocket through most of the atmosphere

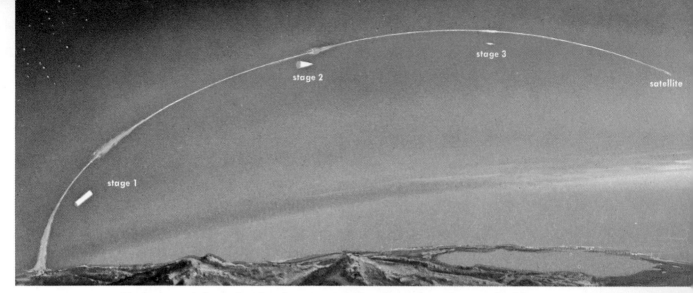

Each stage of the rocket fires in turn, speeding the spacecraft toward orbit

the densest part of the air. The rocket is smooth and streamlined to cut down friction. It shoots straight up, taking the shortest path through the atmosphere.

In about two minutes the rocket is 50 miles high. Stage one has dropped away. Stage two fires, then stage three.

Each stage has vanes placed in the stream of hot gases. They work like rudders. When the vanes are straight, the rocket goes straight. When they are turned, the rocket swerves.

Into Orbit

Then gradually the rocket curves into a path horizontal with the Earth's surface. It is headed eastward, to take advantage of the speed of the Earth's rotation. The rocket has this speed from the start and keeps it by turning toward the east.

The height of the planned orbit has been reached. The rocket is now traveling five miles a second. Firing stops, and the spacecraft separates from the rocket.

Radio signals from the ground start the satellite's instruments working. Panels unfold to face the Sun. The light which they receive is turned into elec-

tricity for operating the radio and other instruments. With panels extended, the craft looks like a strange, misshapen windmill. Streamlining is unnecessary at this height, for there is no air to cause friction and loss of speed.

At the satellite's distance from the Earth, gravity pulls it down 16 feet a second. This falling motion, plus the forward motion at five miles a second, makes a curve that matches the curve of the Earth. This is the satellite's orbit.

Artificial satellites—new tools of astronomy

SHAPES OF ORBITS

What shape is best for an orbit around the Earth? It depends on the purpose of the launching. Take, for example, the launching of the American satellite Midas. In this case scientists wanted to measure the amount of heat reflected from the Earth. They decided on an orbit 300 miles high and nearly circular.

It would be impossible to put a satellite into a perfectly circular orbit. To do this, the satellite's path at the moment of release would have to be exactly horizontal with the Earth's surface. In addition, its speed would have to be exactly matched with its distance from the Earth. To have such a degree of exactness is out of the question. Scientists are satisfied if they come close to it.

For Midas' orbit, a speed of 4.7 miles a second was needed. The launching went according to plan. Midas had about the right speed and was released at about the right height, so it went into an orbit that was nearly circular. Its *perigee*—the point closest to the Earth—was about 300 miles away. Its *apogee*—the point farthest from the Earth—was 340 miles away.

The orbit of every satellite is at least a little elongated—farther across in one direction than another. Such an orbit is called an ellipse. The planets and their moons all travel in elliptical orbits.

For astronauts, nearly circular orbits have been chosen. Then they stay beneath the dangerous radiation belts. To study these belts, scientists choose a very long orbit. Then the satellite passes up and down through the belts, collecting information from various levels.

For a satellite to have a long orbit, it must be launched at a speed of more than five and less than seven miles a second. The greater the speed, the longer the orbit. After launching, the satellite shoots farther and farther from the Earth. Opposite the launching point, it is farthest away—at apogee.

In swinging outward, the satellite slows down. This makes it fall faster. The satellite comes closer and closer to the Earth. By the time it returns to its launching point, it is nearest the Earth—at perigee. Falling speeds it up, so now it swings out toward apogee again. And so it goes around its orbit, swinging far, then falling near, over and over.

If the launching speed is seven miles a second or more, the satellite goes so far away that it does not fall around the Earth. Instead, it falls into an orbit around the Sun. Then it is a small planet.

Different orbits for different purposes

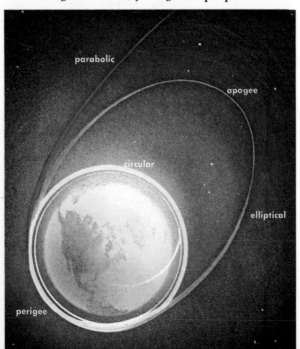

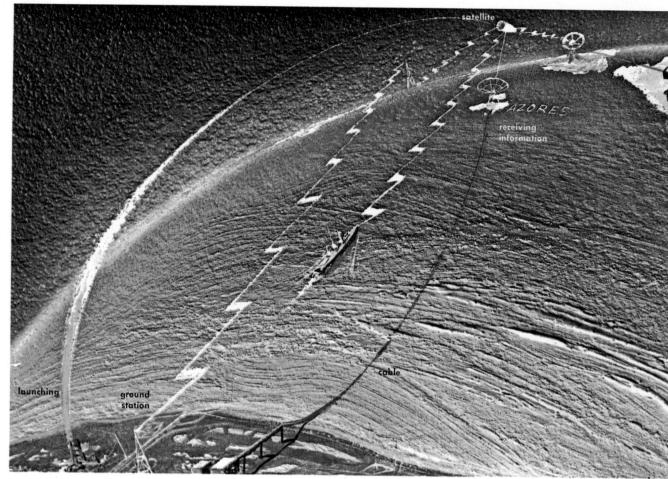

Ground stations give commands, receive information, and track a satellite by radio

Tracking

A spacecraft is tracked mainly from its radio signals. These are received at several ground stations. Since the stations are at different distances from the craft, the signals reach them at slightly different times.

These times are flashed to a center and fed into computers. The computers use the differences between the arrival times to determine the position of the spacecraft moment by moment.

After part of the path has been traced, the computers can predict where the craft will go next. This prediction is checked as more reports come in.

The ground stations also receive information from the spacecraft's instruments. The instruments give signals which are recorded on tape in the craft itself. On command from the ground, the signals are broadcast from the tape.

Broadcasting can go on as long as the batteries of the craft hold out. Since they are recharged with electricity made from sunlight, they can last for years.

To save weight, the batteries are small. As a result, the broadcasts are weak and must be picked up by large dish antennas. These great "ears" are so sensitive that they can track a spacecraft for millions of miles and receive reports about a distant planet.

G FORCE AND WEIGHT

An astronaut need not worry about high speeds. Speed itself is harmless. After all, the Earth carries us around the Sun at 66,000 miles an hour and we do not even feel the motion. That is because it is steady. In a spacecraft, also, steady speed is unnoticeable. The real problem is change of speed—acceleration.

You feel acceleration when riding in an elevator. As it starts upward, your body pushes against the floor with more than normal force. If you were standing on a scale you would push harder on it, and the scale would show that your weight had increased.

Starting down, you become lighter. A scale would show this, too. If the elevator should fall, you would weigh nothing. The scale also would be falling, and you would not be pushing on it with even one ounce of weight.

Normal weight is caused by the pull of gravity at the Earth's surface. When a rocket takes off, its weight becomes much greater than normal, and so does the weight of everything in it. If the rocket and its contents become 7 times heavier, the force of acceleration is called 7 *g*'s. This means it is 7 times the force of gravity at the Earth's surface.

When a spacecraft coasts into orbit, it becomes a falling body. The craft itself has no weight, and everything in it, including passengers, becomes weightless. The effect of gravity is canceled out. This is zero *g*.

For the return to Earth, the craft must be slowed down. This causes a force of about 10 *g*'s, making the craft and contents 10 times heavier than normal.

How Many G's

How much *g* force can a man stand? Before any astronauts were launched, careful tests were made. Men were placed in a whirling machine that gave them as much acceleration as they would have in a rocket.

Next, animals were sent into space. Dogs flew for the Russians. Chimpanzees flew for the Americans. The animals wore space suits tailored for them.

In 1960, a Soviet sputnik carried the dogs Belka and Strelka around the Earth for 24 hours. Cameras took movies which showed how they managed. During launching, the dogs were pressed flat against the floor by *g* force. They could not lift their heads nor raise their paws.

When the sputnik coasted into orbit, the dogs began drifting around the

Space dogs became used to weightlessness

cabin. At first their paws hung limp, as though they were too surprised to do anything. But soon they got used to being weightless and began to eat. After a few orbits around the Earth, they were quite at home, floating around until the sputnik was slowed down. This pressed them flat again but did not injure them. When the sputnik landed, Belka and Strelka jumped out barking happily.

From such experiments, scientists learned that weightlessness causes no harm, at least for short periods. They also studied the effects of *g* force. The animals were checked with instruments, and reports were broadcast on their pulse, breathing, and blood pressure. The men in the whirling machines were observed in the same way.

It was found that a man can stand acceleration best when lying on his back on a cushioned couch. He is also helped by wearing a space suit filled with air. Even so, an acceleration of several *g*'s puts a great strain on him. His arms and legs are too heavy to lift. Breathing is hard work. As long as acceleration lasts, he can do nothing but lie still.

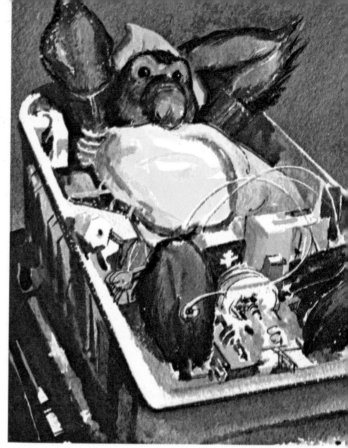

The chimpanzee's health reports were broadcast

The Russians and Americans who became the first astronauts went through many months of careful tests and training. When the rockets were ready, they were ready, too. And because they were well prepared, they flew well and landed safely.

An astronaut lies on a padded couch to reduce g-force strain

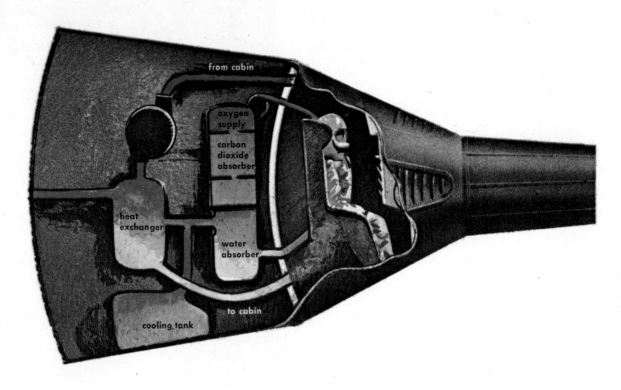

Life support system for astronaut provides oxygen, removes carbon dioxide, controls temperature

SURVIVAL IN SPACE

An astronaut must not be exposed to space, even for a moment. Not only does he need air for breathing, but he also needs air pressure to keep oxygen and other gases dissolved in his blood. If he were exposed to pressureless space, the gases would quickly bubble from his blood, stop his heartbeat and kill him.

The spacecraft is sealed to prevent loss of pressure. An air-conditioning system circulates oxygen, removes carbon dioxide, and controls the temperature of the cabin. In a small spacecraft—one designed for solo flight—the astronaut wears a pressurized suit. He keeps his helmet on although he breathes the air in the cabin. If something should go wrong, he can breathe oxygen from a tank strapped to him. In a large space ship, usually only one astronaut is in a space suit. The others wear ordinary flight suits, which are more comfortable.

Living Without Weight

While a craft is coasting in orbit, the astronaut is weightless. To keep from floating around the cabin, he lies strapped to a couch most of the time. Everything is held firmly in place—food containers, pencils, instruments. If a pencil were to get loose and float around, the astronaut might have a long chase to capture it.

A day's provisions for one man consist of 1⅓ pounds of dried food and 4½ pounds of water. Without gravity, liquids cannot be poured, so the astronaut drinks from plastic squeeze bottles. His solid foods are freeze-dried and packed in bite-sized portions. At mealtime, he adds water to his food with a squirt gun and then squeezes it into his mouth. If stray crumbs drift around, he catches them with a little vacuum cleaner.

The astronaut's body produces about 7 pounds of wastes a day. The carbon dioxide he breathes out is pumped into a tank for chemical treatment. Liquid and solid wastes go into sealed containers.

A Balanced System

It is possible to carry supplies of food, water, and oxygen for a week or two. But what about future trips lasting several months? Supplies for such a period would be too heavy. Another problem would be the accumulation of wastes.

Scientists are working on a scheme to solve both problems. Their idea is to have a balanced system like the one that exists on the Earth, where animal wastes are used by plants, and the plants make food.

A small experimental system works like this: A tank of water containing microscopic plants is kept under strong lights. The tank is enclosed in a sealed chamber. A mouse or other animal lives in the chamber. Oxygen given off by the plants keeps the air fit for the mouse to breathe. The air is bubbled through the tank, so that carbon dioxide produced by the mouse is dissolved in the water for the plants to use.

To make such a system complete, the mouse's liquid and solid wastes would also be used by the plants. And the mouse would depend on the plants for food. The system would work like a sealed, balanced aquarium in which the animal —a fish—feeds on the plants.

The scientists' goal is a plant-man system for spacecraft. Such a system would produce fresh food, water, and oxygen and take care of wastes. It would provide astronauts with the necessities of life all during a long space trip.

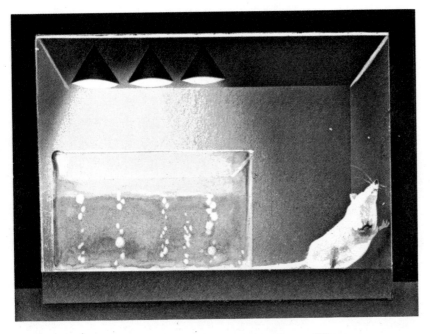

In plant-mouse system, plants in tank absorb carbon dioxide, give off oxygen

DESTINATION: MOON

For several years, scientists have been preparing for man's first voyage to another world. The Moon is their destination. The equipment has been designed; astronauts are trained; landing sites have been studied; and men have already made a test flight around the Moon.

Any lunar flight, whether by a manned or unmanned craft, requires skillful navigation. The target is small, it is a quarter of a million miles away, and it moves around the Earth at about 2,300 miles an hour. Since the flight will take about three days, the rocket is not aimed where the Moon is at the time of launching. It must be aimed at a point in space where the Moon will be about 72 hours later.

The Moon-bound rocket first goes into a parking orbit around the Earth. When it is headed properly, the last stage fires and sends the craft off at escape speed. It coasts away, with the Earth's gravity still tugging at it and gradually slowing it. As the craft approaches the Moon, the Moon's gravity begins to pull it down. To prevent a crash, retro-rockets fire, slowing the craft so that it eases down for a soft landing.

Close-up pictures taken on the Moon's surface show rocks and pebbles in some places, and crumbly soil in others. At first, experts could not decide from the pictures whether the ground was firm enough to support a vehicle. Some thought it might be covered with a blanket of dust in which a vehicle would sink.

This question was answered by a Russian Luna probe in 1966 and an American Surveyor in 1967. In each experiment a spoon-sized shovel dug into the soil, which turned out to be firm enough to support a vehicle.

Flight Plan

According to American plans for the Moon expedition, three astronauts will make the flight. Their craft is built in sections, called modules. At take-off, the men will be in a large command module. Once they are in orbit around the Moon, two of them will get into a small "lunar module" and descend to the surface. The third man will continue orbiting in the command module. Later, the two explorers will return in the lunar module and rejoin him.

With this system, much less fuel will

1. Explorers land on Moon. 2. They return to command module, leave lunar module behind

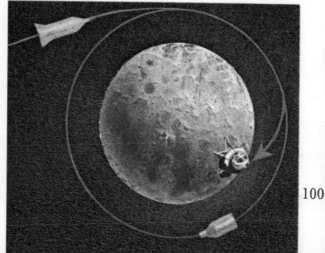
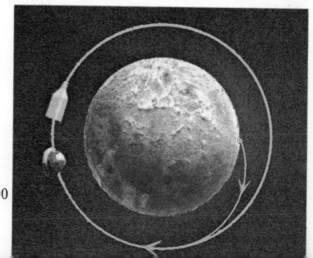

be needed than if the large command module were to land on the Moon. The main fuel supply will remain attached to the command module, to be used for returning to the Earth.

The landing site on the Moon will be somewhere on the visible side, possibly on the great plain called Ocean of Storms. The region has many features that scientists would like to explore. Among them is a large crater named after the astronomer Copernicus. A ring of mountains surrounds it, and mysterious white trails radiate from the crater in all directions.

On the Moon

Imagine the excitement of the explorers as their craft eases down to the surface of the strange world. They feel a jolt, and there they are, on the Moon.

The astronauts open the hatch of their craft and step down on the bare, desert land. Because of the Moon's weak gravity, they weigh only one-sixth as much as they did on the Earth. Their helmets, suits, and oxygen tanks feel light, making it easy to move around.

Here on the Moon, space begins right at the ground. The astronauts' footsteps make no sound, for there is no air to carry sound. They can talk to one an-other only by radio.

The airless space is cold, but sunlight heats up anything it strikes. The ground is very hot. It is well that the explorers' feet are protected by thick asbestos soles. Their suits are a shade of gray that absorbs just enough heat to keep the air inside them warm.

The explorers avoid facing the glare of the Sun, which blazes in the black sky near the horizon. But they admire another heavenly body, a huge bright crescent shining overhead, surrounded by stars. This is the Earth.

Since every minute is precious, the men work quickly at their many tasks. They set up an instrument for counting radiation particles, and another to detect any hits by small meteorites. They observe the nearby mountains, craters, and surface cracks. They measure gravity and magnetism.

The explorers collect samples of soil and rock. They look for iron fragments around the craters—fragments which might show that meteorites blasted the craters. They investigate cracks in the ground to see if any gases are leaking from them. Such gases would mean volcanic activity is going on under the surface. Finally, the two men carefully pack their soil and rock samples. When these

3. Explorers start back toward Earth. 4. Command module approaches Earth

101

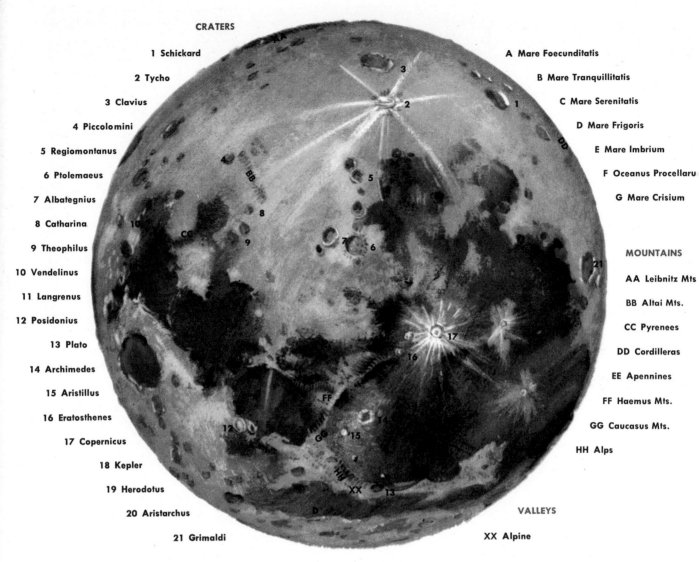

CRATERS

1 Schickard
2 Tycho
3 Clavius
4 Piccolomini
5 Regiomontanus
6 Ptolemaeus
7 Albategnius
8 Catharina
9 Theophilus
10 Vendelinus
11 Langrenus
12 Posidonius
13 Plato
14 Archimedes
15 Aristillus
16 Eratosthenes
17 Copernicus
18 Kepler
19 Herodotus
20 Aristarchus
21 Grimaldi

A Mare Foecunditatis
B Mare Tranquillitatis
C Mare Serenitatis
D Mare Frigoris
E Mare Imbrium
F Oceanus Procellaru
G Mare Crisium

MOUNTAINS

AA Leibnitz Mts
BB Altai Mts.
CC Pyrenees
DD Cordilleras
EE Apennines
FF Haemus Mts.
GG Caucasus Mts.
HH Alps

VALLEYS

XX Alpine

THE MOON AS SEEN THROUGH A TELESCOPE

are studied later in laboratories on the Earth, they will help to answer many questions about the Moon.

Soon it is time for the explorers to take off and join their comrade in the orbiting command module. Before leaving, they perform a little ceremony in the time-honored tradition of explorers. They stack the supplies and instruments which cannot be taken back, and leave a note with them.

The note will tell any future visitors that this is the spot where men first set foot on the Moon. Indeed, the explorers' footprints are on the ground. Perhaps

they will remain there for thousands of years, since there are no rains to wash them away, nor winds to cover them with dust.

Future Expeditions

After the Moon has been well explored, bases will be set up where men can live and work for weeks at a time. By then they will know how to use materials of the Moon for building shelters. Water and oxygen will probably be obtained from minerals in the lunar rock.

Moon bases may serve as stations for

While exploring craters on the Moon, astronauts will see the Earth shining in the sky

expeditions to Mars and Venus. These planets, too, will be surveyed first by instrument-carrying probes. Only when conditions on the planets are known, will it be safe for explorers to visit them.

Later expeditions may be made to Jupiter and other giant planets. Landings on them will be out of the question, since the giants are blanketed with poisonous gases. In addition, their powerful gravity would make escape difficult, if not impossible.

We cannot say now how far men will go in space. But we can be sure of this: Once men have set foot on the Moon, they will want to go beyond it. They will explore more distant worlds, making the dream of the rocket pioneers come true.

After exploratory trips, a permanent base will be built on the Moon

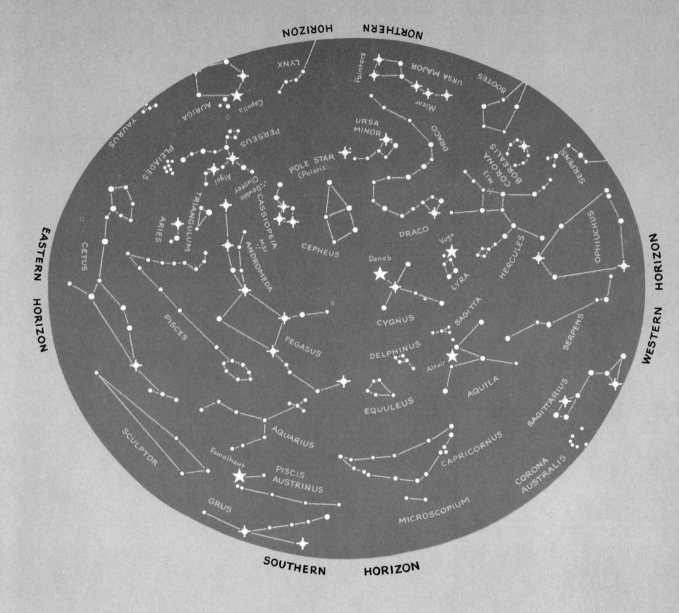

CONSTELLATIONS OF AUTUMN

ABOUT 9 P.M. IN OCTOBER IN MOST OF THE NORTHERN HEMISPHERE

Hold chart overhead with the words NORTHERN HORIZON *toward north.*

STARS

1st magnitude ★
2nd magnitude ✦
3rd magnitude ●
Fainter ·
Star clusters and nebulae ∴

OTHER INTERESTING OBJECTS

Great Nebula M31 in ANDROMEDA
Star clouds and coal sacks in Milky
Way between CYGNUS and SAGITTARIUS
Globular star cluster M13 in HERCULES
Double star cluster between PERSEUS and CASSIOPEIA